Fr
Brockett's
Amazing
Sports
Quizbook

Empire Publications

Manchester

First published in 1999

EMPIRE PUBLICATIONS LTD
62 Charles Street, Manchester M1 7DF

ISBN   1-901-746-09-7

Typeset by
Michael Hubbard
and printed in Great Britain
by MFP Design & Print
Longford Trading Estate
Thomas Street
Stretford
Manchester M32 0JT

Acknowledgements

I would like to thank all the members of my family and friends who have helped me. A special mention to David Rainford for his guidance, and also to Glenn Fleming. An extra special thank you for everybody at Empire Publications: Ashley Shaw, Stuart Fish, John Ireland, Kate Schofield and Mike Hubbard.

I would like to dedicate this to my two best mates Conal and Paul and my little girl Joylin.

Contents

ACTORS

1. Which man is known as 'The Muscles from Brussels'?
2. Before Arnold Schwarzenegger went into films, what was his sport?
3. Michael Jordan acts alongside cartoons in which film?
4. Sylvester Stallone could have been a professional goalkeeper. True or false?
5. Olympic swimmer Johnny Weismuller was most famous for playing which film character?
6. Which star of 'Raging Bull' was told he could have been a professional boxer?
7. At which martial art was Chuck Norris once a World Champion?
8. Errol Flynn competed in which sport at the Olympics?
9. Name the well-known actor who has a Sheffield United tattoo.
10. Which footballer appeared in the 1998 film 'Lock, Stock And Two Smoking Barrels'?
11. Bruce Lee played 'Kato' in which TV series?
12. Which sporting actor's last words were: "That was a great game of golf"?
13. John Wayne had an injury which prevented him from going into which sport?
14. Dolph Lundgren played an adversary in which Rocky film?
15. Which Smith captained England at cricket and went on to become a Hollywood actor?
16. Brian Bosworth went into acting after leaving which sport?
17. Paul Newman starred in which ice hockey film?
18. In which film does Whoopi Goldberg become the coach of an awful basketball team?
19. Jackie Gleason played which character in 'The Hustler'?
20. Colin Firth played the lead in which film, based on a Nick Hornby book?
21. Who played the quarterback in the film 'Mean Machine'?
22. Jack Johnson, the World heavyweight boxing champion played Othello on stage. True or false?
23. Which boxer had a fistfight with Oliver Reed in the film 'Royal Flash'?
24. 'I am the Hippopotamus' and 'The Sheriff and the Satellite Kid' are two films starring which sportsman?
25. Which man won the shot put silver medal at the 1928 Olympics and later became Tarzan?

THREE LIONS

1. A number of England footballers caused £5,000 worth of damage on a plane in 1996 when coming back home from where?
2. Who was the youngest player to play for England in the 20th century?
3. Which England International is in the record books for being the heaviest goalkeeper, reaching 26 stones by the end of his career?
4. Which Englishman scored the quickest ever goal in the World Cup Finals in 1982?
5. What is Nobby Stiles' first name?
6. Which knight was sacked as England manager in 1974?
7. Who still holds the record for scoring the most goals for England?
8. Who said: "Why didn't you just belt it son"?
9. Gary Lineker's last England game was against which country?
10. Which England player was compared to Mary Poppins in 1998?
11. England played which country in an ill-tempered quarter-final of the 1966 World Cup?
12. In 1998 which Blackburn striker told Glenn Hoddle he didn't want his B squad place?
13. 'This Time (We'll get it right)' was the England anthem for which World Cup?
14. Which two England players had a hit with 'Diamond Lights' in 1987?
15. How many Man Utd players made it into Hoddle's final 22 at France '98?
16. Which England Manager played for his country for the first time in 1957 and scored twice?
17. In which year did Peter Shilton make his England debut?
18. Which manager failed to take England to the 1994 World Cup?
19. Who succeeded Alf Ramsey as England manager?
20. What was the name of Glenn Hoddle's infamous faith healer?
21. Who was sent off against Argentina at France '98
22. When England's players were first interviewed at France '98 what did they attempt to slip into every conversation?
23. Which footballer has the middle names Emerson Carlysle?
24. Which Times journalist's interview led, within a week, to the dismissal of Glenn Hoddle as England manager?
25. Which former England striker is ironically known as 'mystic Kev'?

MIXED BAG 1

1. What is the largest victory ever achieved in an official first-class match?
2. Which game can be described as a mini snooker table with mushrooms on it, the idea being to knock balls into holes indirectly?
3. Rachael Heyhoe-Flint is a name most closely associated with which sport?
4. How long is a marathon in kilometres?
5. In 1981 which horse won the Derby by a record 10 lengths?
6. Shirley Crabtree was better known as which larger-than-life character?
7. Which ball do you have to pot last to win a game of pool?
8. In which country was Lennox Lewis born?
9. Lacoste shirts get their name from Rene Lacoste. Which sport did he play?
10. How many players make up a team on court in a game of handball?
11. Stuart Pearce left which club to join Newcastle Utd?
12. 'The Gooner' is a fanzine associated with which football club?
13. In cricket which county is known as the Spitfires?
14. 'Cobb' was a film about which baseball player?
15. Back in 1957 which baseball team left Brooklyn for LA?
16. Which Welshman won the 1979 World Snooker title at his first attempt?
17. What does MVP mean in American sport?
18. In cricket what does it mean if you are out 'c & b'?
19. A 'spare' is scored in which sport?
20. When were goal nets invented in football?
21. Which Swedish boxer became World Heavyweight Champion with a right hand that he labelled 'The Hammer of Thor'?
22. Bob Champion won the Grand National on which horse?
23. When Damon Hill left Williams, which driver replaced him?
24. Who won Britain's only gold at the 1980 Winter Olympics?
25. What colour are Liverpool's home shirts?

BOXING 1

1. Packy East had three boxing bouts, all of which he lost. When asked about them he said: "I was on the canvas more times than Rembrandt". How is he better known?
2. When Terry Marsh was World Champion he also had another job. What was it?
3. Which boxing promoter is known for his distinctive electrified hair?
4. Who bought the title 'Lord of Brighton'?
5. Daniel Alicea was the first boxer to put which British World Champion onto the canvas?
6. Who is the 'Fleetwood Assassin'?
7. How many times did Chris Eubank fight Steve Collins?
8. Alan Minter was a World Champion at which weight?
9. Why would a cornerman put adrenaline on a cut during a fight?
10. Joe Calzaghe comes from which country?
11. What is the lightest weight in professional boxing?
12. What does WBO stand for?
13. Who was the 'Celtic Warrior'?
14. What is the BBBC?
15. HBO is important in boxing. What is it?
16. What is Naseem Hamed's religion?
17. Who was Roberto Duran fighting when he turned round to the referee and said: "No Mas"?
18. Roy Jones played which other sport for the Jacksonville Barracudas on the same day as a title fight?
19. Julio Cesar Chavez is Mexican. True or false?
20. Which colour medal did Robin Reid win at the Barcelona Olympics?
21. Who said this when asked why he shaved his head: "With four sisters running about the house I could never get my hands on a comb"?
22. What is a rabbit punch?
23. In which film does Paul Newman play Rocky Graziano?
24. Which former World Middleweight Champion tragically shot himself in May 1966?
25. How many weights are there in amateur boxing?

ADVERTS

1. Kevin Keegan and Henry Cooper both advertised which aftershave?
2. Which Manchester United player regularly advertises Manchester Arndale Centre?
3. In the Pizza Hut advert who put a paper bag over his head?
4. Which breakfast cereal have Geoff Boycott, Ian Botham, Sharron Davies and Brian Clough all advertised?
5. Name the American Footballer who complained about losing his advertising contracts after being cleared of murder?
6. Ian Rush said, "If I don't drink my milk I'll only be good enough to play for ..." which football team?
7. Graham Taylor sends whom a cake in the Yellow Pages advert?
8. "Be Like Mike" is a slogan in America. Who is Mike?
9. J.R.Hartley was looking for a book on which sport?
10. Which tiger has played volleyball, frisbee and had a great time mountain biking?
11. Which fast food chain did Jonah Lomu, the Underwood brothers and their mum advertise?
12. Eric Cantona, Ian Wright, Robbie Fowler and David Seaman all play football on Hackney Marshes, in which ad?
13. Which wrestler became the voice of Tetley Tea?
14. Even Ian Botham couldn't eat three what?
15. Which former Liverpool player advertised Wash 'n' Go shampoo in 1998?
16. In which advert did Agassi say: "Call me Andre"?
17. Which interesting man advertised Heinz Baked Beans?
18. Sally Gunnell and Will Carling both advertised which tasty product?
19. In 1979 which was the first British football club to have a shirt sponsorship deal?
20. Roy Keane advertised which chocolate product when he visited confession to tell of his football sins?
21. Which footballer starred in an advert for L'Oreal?
22. Steve Backley and Iwan Thomas went naked to advertise whose shoes?
23. Which Heavyweight boxer has advertised Mars, HP Sauce, Kleenex and Persil?
24. "Hello World", were the words used by Nike in their first campaign to advertise which man's prodigious talents?
25. Which coffee does Ian Wright drink after he runs out of petrol?

AGGRO

1. Why is Matthew Simmons infamous?
2. Who did Zola Budd trip up at the Olympics?
3. In 1995 which two Blackburn Rovers team-mates fought each other during a Champions League match?
4. Which England player was punched by a West Ham fan after a 3-0 win against Portugal at Wembley?
5. In 1974, which number was called out by the Lions to 'defend themselves'?
6. Riddick Bowe took an injunction out against which member of his family after she hit him?
7. Marvin Hagler defeated whom in 1980, which in turn led to a riot?
8. Which man set a record in 1987 whilst playing for Man Utd against Southampton in a league match by being sent off after a mere 85 seconds?
9. Shakoor Rana had an altercation with which England cricket captain?
10. In 1998 Alan Shearer was alleged to have kicked which Leicester City player in the head but was cleared?
11. Which Italian footballer sustained a fractured cheekbone at Grimsby Town after a fracas with his manager?
12. Which snooker player was banned for ten months for threatening to have Dennis Taylor shot?
13. In boxing, if a trainer throws a towel in the ring what does it mean?
14. Which tennis player used to say: "You cannot be serious"?
15. In which sport is defence called the back pocket and attack the front pocket?
16. Which show-jumper showed his contempt for judges at Hickstead by giving them the 'V' sign?
17. In 1998 which cricket coach put his job in jeopardy following his remarks about a Sri Lankan bowler?
18. Mike Tyson bit which man's ear?
19. Dennis Rodman is a name from which sport?
20. Tonya Harding attempted to have which opponent dealt with?
21. Johan Le Roux had a lengthy ban from which sport after biting an adversary's ear?
22. Michael Schumacher accused which man of attempting to kill him in 1998?
23. I.D.. is a film about hooligans in which sport?
24. Tommie Smith wore a black scarf on the podium at the Mexico City Olympic Games. What did his protest represent?
25. Which team ran amok in Bournemouth in 1990 after gaining promotion to the old First Division, with fans rioting, looting and assaulting along the way?

INTERNATIONAL CRICKET

1. Why was the first Test Match between England and West Indies in Jamaica abandoned in 1998?
2. Who was the first man in Test history to take 300 Test wickets?
3. Which West Indian test players were known as the three W's?
4. Which Test side does Heath Streak play for?
5. When the Ashes are played in Australia, a Test match traditionally starts on Boxing Day at which ground?
6. Which country holds the record highest Test score of 952-6, achieved against India?
7. Brendan and John Bracewell were two brothers who played cricket for which country?
8. When England toured New Zealand in 1997, which player was allegedly caught smoking an illegal substance in a restaurant?
9. Who is 'Beefy'?
10. Dickie Bird umpired his last Test at which ground?
11. Which former Test cricketers lost their libel case against Imran Khan?
12. Which South African left his country to play 44 Tests for England from 1966 to 1972?
13. What was Don Bradman's Test batting average?
14. England lost the first Test in the 1998 tour of the West Indies, but which bowler took 11 wickets for England?
15. Who was the first professional captain of England?
16. If you get a 'golden duck' in both innings of a Test, what is this called?
17. What is TMS short for?
18. What is the 'Death Rattle'?
19. What did South African cricketer Pat Symcox become the first to do in over 90 years in 1998?
20. Who was Dean Headley's famous cricketing grandfather?
21. Who won the first Cricket World Cup?
22. Following on from that, the first World Cup took place in which year?
23. In 1956 which bowler took all ten Australian wickets in an innings?
24. Which Indian bowler recently emulated that feat by taking all ten Pakistan wickets in an innings?
25. If you were watching the home team play in Harare which country would you be in?

MIXED BAG 2

1. With which sport is the name Carling Bassett associated?
2. How many holes in are there in a Ten Pin bowling ball?
3. The Salford City Reds play which sport?
4. 'When You're Smiling' is a fanzine from which football club?
5. Which Test cricketer won the BBC Sports Personality of the Year in 1975?
6. The golfer Jumbo Ozaki comes from which country?
7. How many players are there on each team in a game of shinty?
8. Which game is played in 2 halves of 30 minutes on a court of 40 metres long by 20 metres wide with goals 2 metres high and 3 metres wide?
9. The film 'Players' is about which sport?
10. Malcolm Cooper won two Olympic golds for Great Britain in which sport?
11. James 'Lights Out' Toney is a name from which sport?
12. From which country do the Olympics originate?
13. Jonty Rhodes is regarded as one of the best fielders in world cricket. Which Test side does he play for?
14. Villa Park is the home of which football club?
15. Petra Felke is a name linked closely with which field event?
16. What is the BAAB?
17. Linford Christie won the 100 metres gold in the '92 Olympics but who was the last Briton before him to achieve the same feat?
18. The 'Toffee Men' is the nickname of which football team?
19. If you were watching the Atlanta Hawks playing the Indiana Pacers what sport would you be watching?
20. Which well-known heavyweight boxer said this? "People may think all boxers are animals. But we are all brothers at the end of the day black, white, yellow or pink. We hug each other after a fight like we are gay."
21. Who plays football at Rugby Park?
22. Which King founded Newmarket as a sporting centre?
23. Which football team was formed first: Sheffield Utd or Sheffield Wednesday?
24. The US Tennis Open takes place at which venue?
25. Bracknell Bees play which sport?

FA CUP 1

1. In 1972 which non-league team knocked Newcastle Utd out of the FA Cup?
2. How many FA Cup finals did George Best appear in?
3. Dave Beasant was the first goalkeeper to save a penalty in the FA Cup final, but who took the penalty?
4. In the history of the FA Cup who is Charles Alcock?
5. Which Second Division team won the FA Cup in 1973?
6. Which player scored in every round of the 1970 FA Cup?
7. In the 1985 final, what happened to Kevin Moran that had never happened before in a final?
8. 1971 he lost in the final and in 1987 he was there again – name the player?
9. Ted MacDougall scored nine goals for which team against Margate?
10. "And Smith Must Score" famously describes a shot that should have won the 1983 FA Cup. Which club's fanzine is named after that description?
11. Who won the 1987 FA Cup?
12. Which team won the FA Cup having supposedly been out for a pub-crawl the night before?
13. Where was the first FA Cup final played?
14. Following on from the previous question, who contested the final?
15. Who are the only non-English team to win the FA Cup?
16. Which Manchester City player scored both for and against his own club in the 1981 final?
17. When was the first FA Cup final?
18. Which team lost the 1983 final and were relegated in the same season?
19. Derek Clark was the first what, playing for WBA in the final of 1968?
20. Which team made the most FA Cup final appearances in the 1980's?
21. Who won the Centenary FA Cup?
22. In 1970 which team became the first to win the Cup after a replay?
23. How many times has Old Trafford hosted the FA Cup final?
24. Wembley hosted its first FA Cup final in which year?
25. Which cricketer won an FA Cup winners' medal in 1950?

ALI

1. What was Ali's name before he changed it?
2. Who was the first boxer to knock down Ali in his professional career?
3. Why did Cassius Clay become Muhammad Ali?
4. Finish Ali's famous catch-phrase: "Float like a Butterfly, sting like a…"?
5. In which year did the 'Thriller in Manila' take place?
6. Ali first used the phrase 'Rope a Dope' after beating whom?
7. Ali won the gold at which Olympics?
8. At which weight did Ali win his Olympic gold medal?
9. "He's a tramp, a bum and a cripple, not worth training for. I'll take him in five." Ali said this about which boxer?
10. In which year did Clay change his name to Ali?
11. When he first became World Champion, who did he beat in 6 rounds to win the title?
12. "I love your show and I like your style. But your pay's so cheap I won't be back for a while." This was said by Ali at the end of which TV show?
13. In which country did the 'Rumble in the Jungle' take place?
14. How many times did Ali fight Joe Frazier?
15. Why was Ali stripped of his world title in 1967?
16. Who out-pointed Ali and broke his jaw in 1973?
17. Ali fought whom in the 'Thriller in Manila'?
18. How many professional fights did Ali have between 1968-69?
19. Henry Cooper knocked Cassius Clay down in the fourth round and then the bell went. What happened next?
20. At which Olympics was the great man given another gold medal?
21. At what age was Ali when he first became World Champion?
22. Who was Ali's last professional fight against?
23. Which boxer was Ali insulting when he said: "You're so ugly that when you cry the tears run down the back of your head."
24. In 1977 Ali beat Alan Evans in a game you wouldn't normally associate with him. He then proclaimed himself World Champion of that sport. Which sport?
25. Ali turned down $500,000 because he didn't want to portray which former World Heavyweight Champion on film?

AUSTRALIAN SPORT

1. When the Australians talk about beating the Poms who do they mean?
2. Which moustachioed bowler used to be greeted by fans with chants of 'Sumo'?
3. When Australia won the Rugby World Cup in 1991, which team did they beat in the final?
4. What did John Bertrand achieve in September 1983?
5. Which boxer came from Hungary, became British and then changed his allegiance to Australia?
6. The game of Aussie Rules has how many scoring posts?
7. The Melbourne Cup takes place at which racecourse?
8. Karrie Webb is a top name in which sport?
9. Which Aussie won the Formula One World Driver's Championship in 1980?
10. How is England's 1932/3 tour of Australia better known?
11. The Brisbane Bandits and the Sydney Blues play which sport?
12. How long does an Aussie Rules game last?
13. The Australian Tennis Open is held in which city?
14. An Aussie Rules team has how many players on the field of play?
15. How many times did Rod Laver win the Wimbledon Men's Singles title?
16. Which Australian finished second in the 200m at the 1968 Olympics?
17. Luc Longley is an Australian who has played which sport professionally in America?
18. Which former England manager failed to take Australia to France '98?
19. Which woman became the first swimmer in Olympic history to win the same event three times in succession?
20. 'Steady Eddie' was a name given to which snooker player?
21. Which Aussie took 355 wickets in 70 Tests?
22. Sydney St.George won 11 grand finals in a row between 1956 and 1966 in which sport?
23. Marjorie Jackson was called 'the Lithgow Flash' by doing the sprint double at which Olympics?
24. What is the SCG?
25. Who was the captain of Australia during the 1997 Ashes series?

MIXED BAG 3

1. Mushtaq Ahmed plays Test cricket for which nation?
2. If England had lost the semi-final of the 1966 World Cup, who would West Germany have played in the final?
3. Which heavyweight World Champion was born Joseph Paul Zukauskar?
4. Goodwood is in which county?
5. How many people make up a netball team on court?
6. FRG were the letters used by which country when competing at sport?
7. What nationality is Christian Gross?
8. Which football team is known as the 'Baggies'?
9. Who played football for Wales aged 45 years 229 days?
10. In pool what is a 'Toilet Licker'?
11. How old was Mike Tyson when he first became World Champion?
12. In baseball who became the first Canadian team to win the World Series?
13. If you saw the Pistons beat the Nuggets what sport would you be watching?
14. The world's oldest annually run marathon is held in which city?
15. How many times is the Chair jumped during the Grand National?
16. Name the speed king who died on Coniston Water on 4th January 1967?
17. The San Francisco Giants play which sport?
18. Tony Doyle received an MBE in 1988 for his services to which sport?
19. What nationality is the footballer Hristo Stoichkov?
20. Sometimes sportsmen and women are tagged 'FEC'. What does that mean?
21. Which country became the first World Netball Champions in 1963?
22. Which sport does Michael Chang play?
23. The Isle of Man compete in the Commonwealth Games. True or false?
24. What is a period of play in polo called?
25. Who do the Barmy Army support?

AMERICAN FOOTBALL

1. How was William Perry better known?
2. The Dolphins come from which city?
3. The Denver Broncos won the Superbowl in 1998 and 1999. Who were the last team before them from the AFC Conference to win the Superbowl?
4. From which city do the Jets hail?
5. Who won the very first Superbowl?
6. Which college team are known as 'The Fighting Irish'?
7. The 'Cheese Heads' support which team?
8. Who was the first quarterback in NFL history to pass for over 50,000 yards?
9. Which is the only American team owned by its fans?
10. The Colts came from where before they moved to Indianapolis?
11. To play the game you need a 'Pigskin'. What is it?
12. The NFL is made up of two conferences. What are their names?
13. How many players are allowed on the field of play for each team at any one time?
14. Which coach is called the 'Big Tuna'?
15. They used to be called the Houston Oilers. How are they now known?
16. Which team lost in every Superbowl between 1991 and 1994?
17. Which NFL team has a horseshoe on the side of the helmet?
18. In the professional game, how many downs do you have to complete ten yards?
19. Born in 1936, this man is regarded as the game's greatest ever running back. Who is he?
20. What did the OJ stand for in OJ Simpson?
21. Walter Payton played which position for the Chicago Bears?
22. What is a 'Hail Mary'?
23. Which team plays at Soldier Field?
24. How many players are there on the field of play in Canadian Gridiron?
25. In minutes, how long is a quarter in American Football?

BADMINTON

1. Sometimes badminton has another name. What is it?
2. Which famous Briton had a nose job in 1981?
3. How wide is a singles court: 17ft, 18ft or 19ft?
4. Paul Erik Hoyer won the gold at Atlanta for which country?
5. When serving, do you serve diagonally or horizontally?
6. In badminton, what is a 'knock up'?
7. Which woman won the first televised female Superstars in this country?
8. What is the least number of points you can score to win a game in badminton?
9. How did badminton get its name?
10. What is the Thomas Cup?
11. Badminton was introduced as an Olympic sport at the Atlanta Olympics. True or false?
12. Badminton and Burghley are both trophies in which sport?
13. Can you score on your opponent's serve?
14. When serving, must you hit the shuttle below or above your waist?
15. Heryanto Abi is a badminton player from which country?
16. Where is the National Training Centre based?
17. How tall is a badminton net from the floor?
18. Why would you spin a racket before a match started?
19. Jo Muggeridge poured a can of which drink over the England manager?
20. Rudy Hartono won the All-England Singles title how many times: 6, 7 or 8?
21. Jack Purcell was the first overseas entrant in the All-England championship. What was his nationality?
22. What is the Uber Cup?
23. Susi Susnati is a top player. Is she from Indonesia, China or South Korea?
24. Between 1903 and 1928 which man won 21 All-England titles?
25. The Thomas Cup was first awarded in which year?

MIXED BAG 4

1. Name the England Bowler affectionately known as "Gus"?
2. For whom did Liam Brady play International Football?
3. Which two football clubs did Robert Maxwell try to merge as the Thames Valley Royals?
4. 154lb is the top weight in which boxing division?
5. What is a switch-hitter in baseball?
6. In 1985 who scored six sixes in one over?
7. What does WBC stand for?
8. How many people make up a hurling team on the field of play?
9. Which football team plays at Bernabeu Stadium?
10. Name the quarterback of the Superbowl winners of 1998?
11. Ivan Mauger and Barry Briggs were two world-beaters from which sport?
12. Who won the first Challenge Cup played at Wembley?
13. Terence Trent D'Arby could have been a professional in which sport?
14. Which weight in boxing is one above flyweight?
15. The Wightman Cup is a trophy linked with which sport?
16. Where is the British Formula One Grand Prix currently held?
17. Where do the football team Fenerbache come from?
18. Where are the NBA team 'The Nets' from?
19. David Wilkie won Olympic gold in which swimming stroke?
20. Sonny Liston defeated whom in 1962 to become World Heavyweight Champion?
21. In which sport would you use a crampon?
22. Which club beat Leeds United in 1971 to win the right to hold the Fairs Cup trophy permanently?
23. 'Blue Heaven' is a book about which football club?
24. Double Carpet are what odds in betting terms?
25. Which boxer was charged with shooting Frank Warren but was later cleared?

ANIMALS

1. In ten pin bowling how many strikes is a Chicken?
2. Which basketball player is known as the 'Worm'?
3. In English football who are the 'Foxes'?
4. Mick the Miller is an animal from which sport?
5. If you bet a Pony how much are you gambling?
6. Bear Bryant is a famous name from which sport?
7. At the start of the 1999-2000 Premiership season who was the manager of the Hornets?
8. The Charlotte Hornets play which sport?
9. During a one-day cricket international between Australia and England at Brisbane in 1983, a pig was let loose on the outfield. It had 'Botham' and 'Eddie' written on it. Who was the Eddie in Question?
10. Why is it a mistake to call the Argentina rugby union team the Pumas?
11. How many times did Red Rum win the Grand National?
12. When hunting what is a 'Charlie'?
13. They used to be called the Worthing Bears, what are they called now?
14. In Super League where do the Bulls come from?
15. How many players are there in a polo team?
16. What does 'Doing the Dog' mean in pool?
17. Richard Fox is a World Champion in which sport?
18. 'Kitten Ball' was the original name for which sport?
19. What do greyhounds chase when racing?
20. In husky-racing how many dogs make up a team in B Class?
21. The Cronulla Sharks play which sport?
22. Which footballer was called 'Crazy Horse'?
23. The Scurry Gold Cup is awarded in which sport?
24. The Iditarod Trail is raced annually in which sport?
25. The 'Clockwork Mouse' was the nickname of which former Formula One World Champion?

SPRINTERS AND ONE-LAP WONDERS

1. Linford Christie won the 100m Olympic gold at which games?
2. Which Athlete wore a pair of gold Nike trainers at the Atlanta Olympics?
3. Which Canadian won the 100m gold at the Atlanta games?
4. Which late female sprinter was known for her jewel-encrusted fingernails?
5. What was Ben Johnson's drug-assisted time in the Seoul Olympics 100m final?
6. Which man was the sensational athlete of the 1936 Berlin Olympics?
7. Which British 400 metre runner announced his retirement in 1998 after he wasn't picked for the European Championships?
8. Who has the forenames Frederick Carlton?
9. Name the runner nicknamed the 'Kansas Cannonball'?
10. What is the maximum number of competitors allowed in a sprint final?
11. Who won the women's 100m title at the 1984 Olympics?
12. Which hurdler won BBC Sports Personality of the Year in 1968?
13. In what time did Michael Johnson win the 200m at the Atlanta Olympics?
14. Who was the woman disqualified in the 1995 World Championships after winning the 200m because she had stepped on her line lane?
15. Between 1977 and 1987 this man was not beaten in 122 races over 400m hurdles. Who was he?
16. How many times has a British athlete broken the World record for the 100m in the 20th Century?
17. Former World record holder Reinaldo Nehemiah left athletics for which other sport?
18. At which Olympics did the first four men in the Olympic 100m final get credited with the same time?
19. What position did Linford Christie finish in the 1996 100m Olympic final?
20. Frankie Fredericks runs for which country?
21. Which British woman finished second in the 100m at the 1960 Olympics?
22. Who was the first Trinidadian to win Olympic gold?
23. Michael Johnson became the second man to hold the 200m and 400m world records simultaneously. Who was the first?
24. Who was the first man to be electronically timed under 10 seconds for the 100 metres?
25. In 1988 Florence Griffith-Joyner set an amazing World record time for the 100m. What was it?

MIXED BAG 5

1. In English football who are the 'Eagles'?
2. What position is DT in American Football?
3. Which football team plays at the Dell?
4. Which country does rally driver Carlos Sainz come from?
5. 122lb is the top weight in which boxing category?
6. Duncan Goodhew won the 100m breaststroke gold at which Olympics?
7. Ritchie Blackmore is a rugby league player from which country?
8. Who sang 'We Can Do it' in 1977?
9. How many times did Lester Piggot win the Derby?
10. Marvin Hagler was undisputed World Boxing Champion at which weight?
11. How many stumps does a bowler aim at?
12. Hasely Crawford won the first Olympic gold for Trinidad and Tobago at which games?
13. Jack Walker is the man behind which football club?
14. 'Final Deliveries' is an anagram of which bowler's name?
15. Until 1999 which was the most visited city on the Tour de France route?
16. Which motorcyclist is known as 'Foggy'?
17. John Madden is a commentator in the United States but for which sport?
18. Which sport is referred to as 'lawn billiards'?
19. Pittodrie is the home of which Scottish football club?
20. Maradona played a large chunk of his career at which Italian club?
21. How did Erica Roe become famous overnight?
22. Which boxing weight is above super featherweight?
23. Every year Didi Seneff gets dressed up as the Devil for which competition?
24. Which British man replaced Nigel Mansell at Williams?
25. Which television comedian once rowed in the Boat Race?

BALLS

1. Who played bowls before fighting the Armada?
2. A 'googly' is a term in which sport?
3. Who became Man City manager in 1995?
4. How many balls are there in a game of billiards?
5. A game of softball is comprised of how many innings?
6. The Veuve Clicquot Gold Cup is awarded in which sport?
7. What is an 'airball' in basketball?
8. GD is what position on a netball court?
9. The 'Federation Internationale Des Quilleurs' is in charge of which sport?
10. 'The Square Ball' is a fanzine from supporters of which football club?
11. Which game has a ball thrown from 60 ft 6 in?
12. Blue, yellow, white and red are all dots on balls played in which game?
13. In ice hockey they don't play with a ball. What do they play with instead?
14. How many balls are there in a game of snooker?
15. Johnny Leach was a Briton who was World Champion in which sport?
16. The World Snooker Championships are held in which city?
17. Which delivery did West Indian cricketer Ellis 'Puss' Achong create?
18. In which game would 2 players have 2 balls each and play on an area of 35 yards by 28 yards?
19. If a ball is described as 'dead' in table tennis what does it mean?
20. Beach volleyball made its first appearance at which Olympics?
21. In which sport must the ball be between 68-70cm in circumference and weigh 410-450gm at the start of the game?
22. Which game is played on an oval pitch with an oval ball?
23. Name the sport governed by the IHF?
24. The President's Cup is a top trophy in which sport?
25. 'It's All About A Ball' is a book by whom?

BOOKS

1. 'The Don' is a book about whom?
2. 'A Lot of Hard Yakka' is a book about which sport?
3. 'The Hand of God' is a book on whom?
4. Nick Hornby wrote a book about the ups and downs of an Arsenal fan. What was it called?
5. When asked to suggest a title for his autobiography, who replied: "The Definitive Volume On The Finest Bloody Fast Bowler That Ever Drew Breath"?
6. Which Argentine's autobiography is called 'Batigol'?
7. Before writing books, Dick Francis was involved in which sport?
8. Roy of the Rovers played for which club?
9. 'Don't tell Kath' is a book by whom?
10. 'You Guys Are History' is which man's autobiography?
11. 'Second Coming' is a book about which sportsman?
12. Which ex-Coventry goalkeeper and snooker presenter's first book was called 'Truth Vibration'?
13. Colin Schindler wrote a book about which club ruining his life?
14. 'A View From The Bridge' is about which football club?
15. Wisden was first published in which year?
16. Which famous bowler had an autobiography called 'Pace with Fire'?
17. Name the Olympic winner who later won the Nobel Peace Prize for his book 'Arms Race'?
18. 'Running Free' is an autobiography by which famous British runner?
19. 'How Long's the course' is the title of whose autobiography?
20. 'Athers' is a book about which cricketer?
21. 'Beating The Field – My Own Story' is a book by which West Indian cricketer?
22. 'Doom to Boom' is the story of which football club?
23. Who was the co-writer on Glenn Hoddle's 'World Cup Diaries'?
24. Which well known sprinter has a book called 'To Be Honest With You' ?
25. Which racing driver wrote a book called 'The Luck of the Irish'?

MIXED BAG 6

1. Lierse is a football team from which country?
2. In 1960 who was the first heavyweight to regain his World Title?
3. Which man won the 400m at the 1998 European Athletics Championships?
4. Don Quarrie was a famous runner from which country?
5. Who was Damon Hill's famous father?
6. Sir Chris Bonnington is associated with which event?
7. Sanath Jayasuriya plays his Test cricket for which nation?
8. With which field event do you associate Dalton Grant?
9. What nationality is the goalkeeper Hans Segers?
10. England won all their games in the 1966 World Cup, apart from a draw against which team?
11. The All-Ireland Finals are always held in which month: August, September or October?
12. How many World Snooker Championships had Jimmy White won up until 1999?
13. Who plays at Blundell Park?
14. Which baseball team used to play in Fulton County Stadium?
15. How many points win a game in badminton?
16. John White thought he had won in 1993, then found out he hadn't. Why?
17. In 1998 who captained Silk Cut in the Whitbread 'Round the World' yacht race?
18. Which famous duo won the BBC Sports Personality of the Year in 1984?
19. Who scored for England in 1956 aged 41 years 248 days?
20. The team used to be called the New Orleans Jazz. What are they now called?
21. Why was a cricket match delayed by 45 minutes on Wednesday 13th August 1999?
22. When Man Utd beat Juventus in the 1999 European Cup semi-final, what was the aggregate score over two legs?
23. Which club bought John Charles from Juventus in 1962?
24. Central Park used to be the home of which rugby league club?
25. What is the correct name for the disc-shaped ball used to fire at the pins in Old English Skittles?

ANGLING

1. An angler would call which fish a 'Snig'?
2. What is 'Chop'?
3. In the Yellow Pages advert who was looking for the book on fly-fishing?
4. What does NFA stand for?
5. Gareth Edwards is a very keen angler but with which sport do we normally associate him?
6. Which England World Cup winner and former Republic of Ireland manager is renowned for his love of angling?
7. Which man wrote 'Stillwater and Fly-fishing'?
8. A 'gonk' is what type of fish in angling?
9. What is a 'baby's head'?
10. Eggs, flavouring and protein powder are rolled into a ball and then boiled. What is this called?
11. What is a 'footballer' or a 'Billy'?
12. What is a 'priest' in Fly-Fishing?
13. Bob Nudd is a former Angling World Champion but what nationality is he?
14. How often do the National Angling Championships take place?
15. Which man associated with snooker, boxing and football devised 'Fish-O-Mania'?
16. Which European country hosted the first World Fly-Fishing Championship in 1981?
17. 'Billy the Fish' is a character from which comic?
18. True or false. The first English Angling Championships took place in 1906?
19. Which man directed the film 'A River Runs through it'?
20. What is a peg?
21. Which former member of The Who owns his own fish farm?
22. Ellem Fishing Club is the oldest club still in existence. Which country does it come from?
23. If you call someone a 'Noddy' what does it mean?
24. What is an 'Arlesley Bomb'?
25. The first World Fresh Water Championship was held in which decade?

AFRICAN SPORT

1. What nationality is Nwankwo Kanu?
2. At which Olympic Games did Zola Budd first compete for Great Britain?
3. Colonel Gadaffi banned team sports in which country?
4. Which sport do you associate with Zimbabwean Nick Price?
5. Graeme Hick was born in Zimbabwe. True or false?
6. Precious McKenzie left South Africa and went to New Zealand. What was his sport?
7. Hogan Bassey was which African country's boxing World Champion?
8. Who was the first non-American to win the US Masters?
9. How old was Paul Adams when he made his South African Test debut?
10. By winning the 400m at the 1972 Olympics, John Akii-Bua became the man from which country to win gold?
11. Eddo Brandes took a one-day hat-trick against England. Which side was he playing for?
12. Which man won the marathon at the Rome Olympics barefooted?
13. The African Nations Cup is contested in which sport?
14. When South Africa won the Rugby World Cup in 1995 who was their captain?
15. 'The Rumble in the Jungle' took place in which African city?
16. Maria Mutola is a runner from which country?
17. Which African first broke the World mile record?
18. Which South African was World Formula One champion in 1979?
19. Who won the 1997 US Golf Open?
20. David Lloyd was in trouble after saying: "We murdered 'em, we flippin' murdered 'em". Who had England narrowly failed to 'murder'?
21. In which South African city is the Newlands cricket and rugby ground?
22. Who won the men's Olympic football gold at the Atlanta Games?
23. Jim Smith, a Zambian farmer and swimmer, had an unusual way of training for the 1990 Commonwealth games. What was it?
24. Roger Milla played football 213 times for which country?
25. Which South African won the men's marathon at the Atlanta Olympics?

WORLD CUP 1

1. In 1966 which dog found the World Cup?
2. What does FIFA stand for?
3. Who won the first World Cup in 1930?
4. Leading on from that, which team lost in the final that year?
5. Name the commentator who uttered the immortal words: "They think its all over ... it is now"?
6. 'Cinnamon Stick' was the B-side of which World Cup record?
7. Which country hosted the 1982 World Cup?
8. Brazil won the World Cup for the third time in which year?
9. In 1994 Roger Milla became the oldest man to play in the World Cup Finals when Cameroon played Russia, how old was he?
10. With nine goals, who was the top scorer in the 1966 World Cup Finals?
11. In France '98 which team were called the Reggae Boyz?
12. If West Germany had lost in their semi-final in 1966, who would England have faced in the final?
13. Which country hosted the 1950 World Cup?
14. Who was the Colombian defender who was shot dead after scoring an own goal in the 1994 World Cup?
15. At the 1982 Finals who became the youngest player to appear in the World Cup Finals?
16. The first World Cup was in 1930, then 1934 and 1938, but which year was next?
17. Who was known as 'Der Kaiser'?
18. England got a surprise defeat in the 1950 finals by losing to which team?
19. How many World Cup finals did Maradona appear in?
20. When England won the 1966 World Cup, which player wore the No 16 shirt?
21. When Brazil won the World Cup in 1962 who did they beat in the final?
22. By qualifying for the World Cup in 1994, which squad received a Rolls Royce apiece?
23. Mario Kempes was the top scorer at which World Cup?
24. Jimmy Greaves played in the 1966 World Cup final. True or false?
25. Franz Beckenbauer made how many appearances at World Cup Tournaments?

MIXED BAG 7

1. Where do the Astros baseball team come from?
2. What nationality is the cyclist Abraham Olano?
3. Mervyn King is a name connected with which sport?
4. Shaquille O'Neal played for which club before joining the LA Lakers?
5. Which Paul has played for West Ham, Man Utd, Inter Milan, Liverpool and Middlesbrough?
6. Mohammad Al-Fayed is the man behind which football club?
7. St Andrews is regarded as the home of which sport?
8. In a nine-ball pool set what colour is the number 2 ball?
9. Alec Stewart plays cricket for which county?
10. Which football team plays at Saltergate?
11. What did the CB stand for in the famous sportsman CB Fry?
12. At the 1964 Olympics, who won the boxing heavyweight gold medal?
13. What is the WBO?
14. Which football country plays in red and white checked shirts?
15. Who was the first Englishman to win an Olympic figure skating title?
16. The Derby Storm play which sport?
17. Name the British man who won the 400m title at the 1986 and 1990 European Athletics Championships?
18. Jacques Villeneuve replaced whom as a driver for Williams?
19. When Germany won Euro '96, who did they beat in the final?
20. At what age can a player join the Seniors Golf Tour: 45, 50 or 55?
21. 'Back Home' was England's World Cup song in which year?
22. Brazil was the first country to win the World Cup three times. True or false?
23. Galina Zybina was the first woman to throw what over 50ft?
24. Which football club is known as the Rams?
25. Which Test team scored a world record 952 runs against India in September 1997?

BASKETBALL

1. Who was Dr James Naismith?
2. How many people make up a team on court?
3. Patrick Ewing is a name associated with which NBA club?
4. Which player got his name from a Japanese steak?
5. In English basketball, where do the Giants come from?
6. Apart from his behaviour and his ability, which player is noted for his weird hair?
7. They use to be called the Washington Bullets, what are they now called?
8. Spike Lee is a fan of which basketball team?
9. Which city do the Supersonics come from?
10. How many points do you get from scoring 'Down Town'?
11. What does MVP stand for?
12. 'Butter' is a term in basketball. What does it mean?
13. When Jack Nicholson is making a film he puts it in his contract that he must have time off to watch the home games of which team?
14. 'Bad As I Wanna Be' is a book by which basketballer?
15. The Alamodome is the home court of which NBA team?
16. In the NBA who is called the 'Glove'?
17. Who in 1998 became the youngest player to be in the starting line-up of an NBA All-Star game?
18. Where do the Detroit Pistons plat their home games?
19. In the NBA what are the Atlantic, Central, Midwest and the Pacific?
20. Which team plays at MSG?
21. John Havlicek holds the record in the NBA for playing the most times for one team, 1270. What was the team?
22. Before she had pop songs high in the charts, Paula Abdul was a cheerleader for which NBA team?
23. What is the female equivalent of the NBA called?
24. Which is the only country other than America to win the Olympic gold in men's basketball?
25. Which basketball player started his professional career as Lew Alcindor?

FIELD EVENTS

1. The Hop, Skip and Jump is better known as which Olympic event?
2. Tina Lillak is a name connected with which event?
3. What colour flag indicates a fair throw in the shot put?
4. There is a stop board in the discus. True or false?
5. In the long jump the distance is measured to the nearest what?
6. 'Winning Mind' is a book by which British athlete?
7. What is the first throwing event in the decathlon?
8. Which man revolutionised the high jump in 1968?
9. Who was the first man to jump over 6 metres in the pole vault?
10. In which field event did women compete for the first time at the 1999 World Athletics Championships?
11. What distance was Bob Beamon's long jump world record?
12. The heptathlon has how many throwing events?
13. From December 1956 to June 1967, Iolanda Balas won 140 consecutive competitions in which event?
14. In 1965 Randy Matson became the first man to throw the shot over which distance: 60ft, 65ft or 70ft?
15. Sensational singer Johnny Mathis was ranked in World's top 100 at which sporting event?
16. Which man was the first to break the high jump World record by using the Fosbury Flop technique?
17. In the shot putt, if you had a tie for first place how would you decide the winner?
18. With which field event would you associate Mick Hill?
19. Udo Beyer dominated which event for over 10 years?
20. How many pole vault World titles has Sergei Bubka won?
21. What is the penultimate event in the Decathlon?
22. An athlete has how many attempts to clear a height in the high jump?
23. In the 1924 Olympics Clarence Hauser won which 2 field events? (A point for each)
24. In which event would you use a 'plant box'?
25. The Western Roll is a technique in which event?

NICKNAMES

1. Mirutus Yifter or 'Yifter the Shifter' won the 5,000m and 10,000m double at the 1980 Olympics. What nationality was he?
2. In cricket, who are the Spitfires?
3. Ron 'Chopper' Harris was a hardman who played football for which club in the 1960's and 70's?
4. Konishki retired from sumo after illness and injuries but what was his nickname?
5. What was Wade Dooley's nickname?
6. Who has got a best mate called 'Five Bellies'?
7. Which Essex cricketer is called 'Wallace' because of his prominent ears?
8. 'Bite yer legs' was the nickname of which footballer?
9. Which football team is called the 'Saints'?
10. 'The Cinderella Man' was the name of which boxer?
11. In baseball who is known as the 'Big Hurt'
12. Which Irish boxer has the nickname, the 'Pocket Rocket'?
13. 'Super Brat' was a name for which tennis star?
14. Which baseball legend was called 'Mr. October'?
15. 'Iron Horse' was a legend in which sport?
16. In the Benetton Racing team which driver did the mechanics nickname 'Brucie'?
17. Who has the nickname 'America's Team'?
18. Which jockey was called 'the Shoe'?
19. In rugby league who are the 'Chemics'?
20. Name the large golfer known as the 'Walrus'?
21. Who was the 'Bronx Bull'?
22. Which rugby ground is sometimes referred to as the Cabbage patch?
23. Who is the 'Punchin Preacher'?
24. Who was known as 'King Kenny'?
25. Which heavyweight boxer is called 'The Real Deal'?

BASEBALL

1. Where do the Braves come from?
2. What is a fielder's glove called?
3. Marilyn Monroe married which baseball star?
4. Describe what a triple play is in baseball?
5. How many people make up a baseball team when fielding?
6. Which team were once known as the 'Big Red Machine'?
7. The position 'SS' describes which player?
8. How much does a baseball weigh: is it just over 5oz, 8oz or 10oz?
9. The Dodgers came from which place before moving to LA?
10. In 1969 an expansion team won the World Series for the first time. Which team?
11. Who plays at Turner Field?
12. How did a 12-year-old called Jeffrey Maier help the NY Yankees get into a World Series which they eventually won?
13. The World Series is the best of how many matches?
14. Which baseball great was Rookie of the Year in 1948 aged 42?
15. Why was a player called 'Shoeless' Joe Jackson banned for life from playing by the baseball authorities?
16. Madonna acted in which baseball film?
17. Who holds the record for playing the most consecutive games?
18. Which team threw the World Series in 1919?
19. Which team used to be called 'The Mistake by the Lake'?
20. In 1998 Sammy Sosa and Mark McGuire were both chasing which record?
21. How many innings does each side have unless there is a tie?
22. Who was the first black man to play Major League Baseball in the States?
23. Wesley Snipes and Robert De Niro star in which baseball film?
24. Who was called the 'Georgia Peach'?
25. How many home runs did Babe Ruth hit in his career?

MIXED BAG 8

1. Ronaldo and his Brazilian chums played football in an airport in whose advertisement?
2. Welford Road is the home of which rugby union team?
3. A 'king pair' is a term from which sport?
4. In British sport, what sport does Carl Prean play?
5. Which football club do you associate with Steve Bull?
6. Ian Wright played for which team before Arsenal?
7. In Polo how long is a Chukka: 7 and a half minutes, 10 Minutes or 12 Minutes?
8. Which boxer was called the 'Celtic Warrior'?
9. What nationality is the Grand Prix driver Mika Hakkinen?
10. Betty Uber is a name from which sport?
11. In rugby union, how many points do you get for converting a try?
12. The 2,000 and 1,000 Guineas take place at which racecourse?
13. What have Gay Trip in 1970, Ben Nevis in 1980 and Mr Frisk in 1990 have in common?
14. "I wanted her because she was Miss World and she wanted me because I was George Best." Who was the woman in question?
15. Steve Davis is the nephew of the snooker legend Joe Davis. True or false?
16. The 1982 World Cup was held in which country?
17. What does PGA stand for?
18. Des Drummond had exceptional pace and played which sport?
19. The Solheim Cup is a trophy in which sport?
20. In 1998 which North East team were announced as the latest addition to Super League?
21. Davor Suker is a striker from which country?
22. In Boxing what is a 'glass jaw'?
23. Gay Meadow is the home of which football club?
24. Ben Hogan was a top sportsman in the 1940's and 1950's in which sport?
25. Man Utd bought Bryan Robson from which club?

BETTING

1. What is a score in betting terms?
2. What is Tic-Tac?
3. "If I had the choice of a night with Raquel Welch or going to a betting shop, I'd choose the betting shop." Which talented footballer said this?
4. Which former Arsenal man was the only Middlesbrough player to make the France '98 squad?
5. What is a Heinz?
6. If a horse is described as a 'buzzer', what does it mean?
7. What is a settler?
8. Who were the two Australian Cricketers who backed England to win the third Test in 1981 at 500-1?
9. Which Belfast bookie was the former manager of Barry McGuigan?
10. If you bet when the odds are an apple core, what are your odds?
11. Theodore was a horse who won which Classic in 1822 priced at 200-1?
12. Who captained England at the 1962 World Cup and then went on to become a bookie?
13. In which year did betting shops became legal in this country?
14. In 1989 which famous baseball player turned manager was banned for life for betting on the outcome of matches?
15. If you bet a monkey how much money are putting on?
16. Which Arsenal player won at France '98 and then shortly afterwards won £17,000 on a fruit machine?
17. In 1919 bookies fed an apple laced with powdered glass to a hot favourite called 'The Panther' in which Classic race?
18. Which Chancellor of the Exchequer announced the first tax on betting in 1926?
19. In 1919 who won the World Series after the other team supposedly chucked it?
20. Who played the male lead in the film 'The Hustler'?
21. How was a bookie killed at Royal Ascot in 1930?
22. Bobby Riggs deliberately lost games in which sport so that the odds on him winning future matches would go up?
23. What is a sleeper?
24. John Prescott said at the Labour Party conference: "The only Tory you should bet on these days is..." Which Tory?
25. Which football club got into trouble in 1990 after it was revealed that the chairman and then manager had a bet on them losing an FA Cup match against Newcastle in 1988?

SCANDAL AND OUTRAGE

1. In which year was Mike Tyson sentenced to six years' imprisonment?
2. Which footballer was sentenced to three months at Ford open prison in 1984 for drink-driving and assaulting a police officer?
3. Name the Englishman who was ranked No15 in the world in tennis in 1983, who hit the headlines over his National Front connections?
4. Which tabloid was accused of 'Jingoistic Gutter Journalism' after splashing with this headline "Achtung Surrender for you Fritz ze Euro '96 Championships are over"?
5. Who caused a scandal by talking about 57 old farts?
6. Why was Tonya Harding banned from competitive skating for life?
7. Which West Ham player caused outrage by appearing in a Man Utd shirt before he signed for them?
8. In 1995 which player stormed out of Wimbledon after accusing the umpire of incompetence?
9. Ed Giddins received an 18 month ban from cricket for doing what?
10. Who caused outrage in America by performing a black power salute at the 1968 Olympics, during the National Anthem, when he received the gold for the 200m?
11. Which team were England playing when Michael Atherton was involved in the 'dirt in the pocket' scandal?
12. At which Olympics was Ben Johnson disqualified?
13. If we believe the newspapers, David Mellor was allegedly in which football top whilst getting his toes sucked?
14. Lester Piggott was sentenced to three years' jail for which crime?
15. Which team were Man Utd playing when Eric Cantona kung-fu kicked a fan?
16. Why was Latrell Sprewell banned from playing Basketball during nearly all of the1998 season?
17. Who was John Wayne's nephew who retired from Heavyweight boxing after testing HIV positive?
18. Which bigoted golfer, when asked what he thought Tiger Woods would serve at his Master's Dinner menu, replied: "I hope it won't be fried chicken and collared greens, or whatever the hell they serve".
19. Who is better known as 'Teflon Don'?
20. Which ex-Wimbledon player later joined Chelsea and was accused of assaulting a taxi driver?
21. Which Golden Boot winner had previously been banned over a bribery scandal?
22. Which former Crystal Palace chairman found himself in hot water over racist remarks?
23. "A case of the shit hitting the fan", which incident does this quote describe?
24. What did umpire Ross Emerson do to inflame Sri Lankan captain Arjuna Ranatunga in 1999?
25. Why did the 'transmigration of souls' hit the headlines in February 1999?

MIXED BAG 9

1. A Formula One win nowadays is worth how many points?
2. Henry Rono was a runner from which country?
3. During both World Wars the Derby was held at which course?
4. Name the two Cowdreys who captained England at cricket?
5. If a boxer is having 'beard problems' what does it mean?
6. In America, Allen Iverson was voted Rookie of the year in 1997 for which sport?
7. Which race was run first – the 1,000 or 2,000 Guineas?
8. Which city do the American Football team the Steelers come from?
9. Which Scottish football team play at Dens Park?
10. Wigan signed Martin Offiah from which club?
11. The AAA Championship is in which sport?
12. What nationality is the jockey Steve Cauthen?
13. Where did Pele play in his first World Cup?
14. In the NFL, which team has a star on the side of its helmet?
15. How many times did Joe Frazier fight Ali?
16. In English football who plays at the Stadium of Light?
17. In cricket it's a wicketkeeper – what is the equivalent in baseball called?
18. Andrew Coltart is a golfer from which country?
19. Which Grand Prix takes place at Interlagos?
20. The decathlon has two throwing events on the second day. What are they?
21. Who do Scotland mean when they talk about the 'Auld Enemy'?
22. Which Southern football team are known as the Seagulls?
23. Which county cricket team were re-labelled the 'Steelbacks' for the 1999 season?
24. Name the Canadian snooker player who had a groovy moustache and a liking for beer after beer?
25. Who hosted the 1954 Commonwealth Games?

BIKES

1. What does the TT stand for in the Isle of Man TT Race?
2. Ice speedway originates from which country?
3. Barry Sheene invariably drove his bike with the same bike number. Which number?
4. In speedway what are 'Flickers'?
5. What nationality is Michael Doohan?
6. Assen is a track in which country?
7. What does WSB stand for?
8. Which famous American stuntrider had a skycycle?
9. Graham Walker won the TT, but who is his more famous son?
10. Who was the first man to win the Formula One Championship and the World Motorcycle Championship?
11. Who starred of the film 'No Limit' in which the hero wins the TT?
12. Name the famous motorcycle champion from Blackburn?
13. Which music man starred in 'Silver Dream Machine'?
14. Who won BBC Sports Personality of the Year in 1959?
15. Which American rider broke his back at the Italian Grand Prix in 1993?
16. Which speedway team ride at Foxhall Heath?
17. Who was 'Mike the Bike'?
18. When was the first TT race on the Isle of Man held?
19. In 1976 which Briton won the 500cc World Championship?
20. Honda is a bike company from which country?
21. What is the alternative name for scrambling?
22. In Britain what is the ACU?
23. Which former Blue Peter presenter used to host 'Kick Start'?
24. Steve McQueen attempts to cross the border on his bike in which film?
25. In 1993 which three times 500cc Champion crashed and became paralysed from the waist down?

BIRDS

1. In golf, which is better: an eagle or an albatross?
2. Which Football League team are known as the 'Robins'?
3. Which British man became a superstar overnight by finishing last in the ski-jumping at the Calgary Winter Olympics?
4. Larry Bird was a player and is now a coach in which sport?
5. The Sydney Swans play which sport?
6. Name the football team nicknamed the 'Owls'?
7. In cricket what is a 'duck'?
8. What is a 'dead duck' in American Football?
9. Geoff Capes is known for breeding what types of bird?
10. Who are the Canaries in footballing terms?
11. In pigeon racing all birds must start from the same point. True or false?
12. In Ten Pin Bowling what is a 'turkey'?
13. The Detroit Red Wings play which sport in America?
14. In football who are known as the 'Bluebirds'?
15. Dickie Bird is a name synonymous with which sport?
16. Who won the 1991 World Snooker Championship?
17. Which symbolic birds are released at the opening ceremony of the Olympics?
18. The cockerel is the emblem of which rugby country?
19. Which county cricket team are called the 'Hawks'?
20. With which sport would you associate the Eastbourne Eagles?
21. In Super League what type of bird are Sheffield?
22. Larry Bird played his NBA basketball for which club?
23. Which speed king had a car called Bluebird in the 1930's?
24. Martin Crowe is a famous cricketer from which country?
25. 'Cock A Doodle Do' is the fanzine of which football club?

BOATS

1. What is the nautical term for right?
2. Matthew Pinsent rowed for which University in the boat race?
3. To the nearest mile, how long is the university boat race?
4. How many make up a team in canoe polo?
5. "I've had enough. If anyone ever sees me near a boat again they can shoot me." So said which Olympian?
6. The Boat Race was first televised in 1938. True or false?
7. Which man was rescued from his capsized yacht in January 1997 after entering the solo Round the World race?
8. In 1998 which University had the heaviest ever team to row in the boat race?
9. The Princess Elizabeth Cup is awarded every year at which event?
10. Greta Fredroksson won six Olympic canoeing golds for which country?
11. Who was Steve Redgrave's partner in the coxless pairs at the Seoul Olympics?
12. It's not called left on a boat, but what?
13. In sailing what is a 'big boy'?
14. What nationality is Chay Blyth?
15. The America's Cup was inaugurated in which year?
16. In 1976 which yachtswoman became the fastest woman to cross the Atlantic single-handedly?
17. Cowes is Britain's longest running Yachting Regatta. True or false?
18. Who had a boat called Gypsy Moth III?
19. How did Sue Brown hit the sporting headlines in 1981?
20. Who was the skipper of Silk Cut in the 1998 Whitbread round the world race?
21. What are the two stations in the Boat Race?
22. By 1999 how many consecutive Olympic golds had Steve Redgrave won?
23. In 1955 which man was the first to exceed 200mph in a boat?
24. Name the famous sportsman who was refused admission to the Titanic because he was black?
25. Greg and Johnny Searle won Olympic gold at Barcelona in which event?

MIXED BAG 10

1. Ato Boldon runs for which country?
2. Who retired as FIFA President in 1998 having been President for 24 years?
3. Milton Keynes Kings play which sport?
4. Which cricket county is known as the 'Sabres'?
5. For how many World Cup Finals did the England team qualify during the 1970's?
6. Maurice Lindsay is a name associated with which sport?
7. Is the Oaks raced over: 1 mile, 1 mile 4 furlongs or 2 miles?
8. The Chicago Cubs and the St.Louis Cardinals play which sport?
9. Which skater was BBC Sports Personality of the Year in 1980?
10. In 1986 who ended a 10-year winning streak in the university boat race for the opposition?
11. Leyton Orient play at the Victoria Ground. True or false?
12. In 1994 which England bowler took 9-57 at the Oval against South Africa?
13. Barry Sheene advertised which aftershave?
14. Who was England's cricket captain after Ray Illingworth?
15. Tina Lillak was a javelin thrower from which country?
16. The Chamsil Stadium was the venue for which Olympics?
17. Emlyn Hughes left Liverpool for which club?
18. In rugby union who was known as the 'Blackpool Tower'?
19. Angelo Dundee was a famous coach in which sport?
20. How many Formula One World Drivers' Championships did Stirling Moss win?
21. Which Brendan 'discovered' Naseem Hamed?
22. Does a Canadian canoe have a paddle with one or two blades?
23. What is Gary Lineker's middle name?
24. Poule D'essai Des Pouliches is the French equivalent of which English Classic horse race?
25. Which Swiss city held the European Athletics Championships in 1954?

BODIES AND INJURIES

1. The Bodyline Series took place in which country?
2. In 1992 which British athlete pulled his hamstring in the Olympic 400m semi-final and had to be helped over the finish line by his dad?
3. Which British driver was told his sporting days were numbered after suffering a very bad crash at Brands Hatch in 1988, but went on to make his Grand Prix debut in Brazil in 1989 and score 4 points?
4. The American Lance Armstrong, who made a come-back after fighting cancer, is a former World Champion in which sport?
5. Which baseball player played 2130 games for the New York Yankees and died of a disease that took his own name?
6. Who won the heavyweight boxing gold because the first choice, Buster Mathis, had broken his thumb in training?
7. Paul Lake retired from which football club in 1996 after having a long-term injury?
8. Tommy Armour won the US Golf Open in 1927 with one what?
9. Who played in the 1956 FA Cup final with a broken neck and still won?
10. Michael Schumacher fractured his leg at which Grand Prix in 1999?
11. Which England fast bowler shattered a knee while bowling against New Zealand in 1992?
12. Which man played for West Brom, Man City, Nottingham Forest and Everton with a hole in his heart?
13. In boxing what is a 'mouse'?
14. Which Spurs player made over 550 appearances for his club despite the disadvantage of being a diabetic?
15. When H Redl competed at Wimbledon in 1946 what was unusual about him?
16. Jockey Walter Swinburn was seriously injured in February 1996 at which racecourse?
17. Which England bowler played the starring role in the 'Bodyline' series?
18. In 1982 which well-known British middle-distance runner lost his whole season after falling on some church railings?
19. Which England and Middlesex cricketer lost four toes in a boating accident whilst touring the West Indies?
20. Which boxing commentator has a wooden leg?
21. 'Brian Moore's Head' is a fanzine from which football club?
22. Which former World Middleweight Champion committed suicide in May 1966?
23. Steve Waugh and Jason Gillespie both sustained injuries going for the same cricket ball in 1999, in a Test match against which side?
24. Fabio Casartelli died in 1995 in which famous competition?
25. Footballer David Busst unfortunately had his career ended when Coventry City were playing which team?

SNOOKER

1. If you pot red, black, red, green, red and yellow, how high is your break?
2. Which player had the nickname 'Dracula'?
3. Stephen Hendry appeared on 'This Is Your Life' at what age?
4. After being 7-0 down in the 1985 World Snooker final, who went on to win it?
5. Jim Davidson hosts which TV quiz show based on snooker?
6. How many times did Steve Davis win the World Championships in the 80's?
7. The player James Wattana is from which country?
8. Which Australian was known as 'Steady Eddie'?
9. Which instantly recognisable snooker player from Canada wore flares, enjoyed a beer and had a massive stature?
10. Which 150-1 outsider won the Embassy World title in 1986?
11. Cliff Thorburn had a nickname. What was it?
12. The Crucible Theatre is in which city?
13. Who knocked Stephen Hendry out of the 1998 World Championship?
14. Which player was fined £20,000 for assaulting an official in 1996?
15. Which snooker player was a former apprentice jockey, barman and tailor's cutter?
16. Which player, from the old school, carried the Olympic torch in 1956?
17. Cliff Thorburn said this about whom: "You have as much class as my backside"?
18. "If I had to make a choice between staying married and playing snooker, snooker would win." Who said this?
19. Who was the first woman to compete in the World Snooker Championship?
20. Who won the first fourteen World Snooker Championship titles?
21. In which year did Steve Davis become BBC Sports Personality of the Year?
22. Which novelist and politician is involved in the administration of snooker?
23. In 1985 Stacy Hillyard was the first woman to do what in a competitive match?
24. Which snooker referee was renowned for his 'teddy boy' looks?
25. What is a 'miss' on the green baize?

MIXED BAG 11

1. Amanda Coetzer is a tennis player from which country?
2. Where do the Seattle Seahawks play?
3. Magic Johnson played his basketball at, and now partly owns, which club?
4. Until 1998 how many World Snooker finals had Jimmy White appeared in?
5. In 1970 which football club won the League Cup and the European Cup Winners' Cup?
6. When Nadia Comaneci scored a perfect ten in 1976, what apparatus was it on?
7. Who is the Lord of Brighton?
8. What is the lightest weight in amateur boxing?
9. In which sport is Ed Morrison a top referee?
10. In America's NBA, The Heat come from which Florida city?
11. Which modern British World Heavyweight Boxing Champion has also done a bit of panto?
12. Who became the England football manager in 1982?
13. In Super League who are the 'Tigers'?
14. In 1998 who became the new President of FIFA?
15. What nationality is the runner Said Aouita?
16. Turf Moor is the home ground of which football club?
17. Who is the 'Herminator'?
18. In 1974 the British Lions toured South Africa playing 22 matches. How many did they win?
19. Which man won both the 1984 and 1988 Olympic 100m finals?
20. Who was the second black man to play football for England?
21. The 2,000 Guineas is held at which racecourse?
22. Ball girls where introduced at Wimbledon in which year?
23. In 1971 the value of a try in rugby union was changed to four points. What was it previously?
24. Frank Warren promotes which sport?
25. Ben Hogan competed in one British Open and won it. At which course was it held?

BOXING 2

1. In competitive amateur boxing at senior level, how many rounds do the bouts last?
2. Elvis played a boxer in which 1962 film?
3. Sugar Ray Leonard was named after Ray Charles. True or false?
4. Which man lost his bout for the light middleweight gold at the Seoul Olympics despite battering his South Korean opponent?
5. In professional boxing how long does a round last?
6. Which boxing promoter served four years in jail for killing a man over a debt?
7. Is cruiserweight a weight in amateur boxing?
8. In boxing what is a 'Switch Hitter'?
9. Homicide Hank was the nickname of which fighter?
10. Regarded as one of the best boxers of all time, he was born Walker Smith Jr. Under which name did he fight?
11. In boxing what does 'boiling down' mean?
12. Ken Buchanan was World Champion at which weight?
13. Who was the former Merchant Navy cook from Leamington Spa who became World Middleweight Champion?
14. 'The Hitman' was a nickname for whom?
15. Roberto Duran's home country was?
16. Which boxer won the light welterweight gold at the Montreal Olympics?
17. 'Raging Bull' was the story of which boxer?
18. In professional boxing, how long do fighters rest in between rounds?
19. What is the top weight for boxers in the lightweight category. Is it 130lb, 133lb or 135lb?
20. Which boxer was born Rocco Barbella?
21. Who was the first man to stop Chris Eubank in his professional career?
22. To win a Lonsdale Belt what do you have to do?
23. The Golden Gloves is a trophy in which country?
24. Which weight is above light heavyweight?
25. Michael Bolton could have been a professional boxer. True or false?

FIRSTS 1

1. Who was the black man to play for South Africa?
2. Who was the first million-pound footballer in this country?
3. Where were the first recorded Olympic Games held?
4. Who was the first goalkeeper to save a penalty in an FA Cup final?
5. Apart from the Home Nations, no International side had ever beaten England at home in an International until 1953. Name the team who did.
6. Who was the first woman to train a Grand National winner?
7. Which club gained the distinction of becoming the first British club to win the European Cup?
8. At which Olympics was the photo-finish first used?
9. Barbara Bullrick is generally recognised as Britain's first female professional what?
10. Danny Millman was crowned the first World Champion of which sport in 1964?
11. Who won the first Ryder Cup?
12. Boris Becker was the first unseeded man to win Wimbledon in the Open era. True or false?
13. New Zealand won the very first Rugby World Cup. Who did they beat in the final?
14. Johnny Weismuller became the first to do what in under a minute?
15. Who was the first person to score a 147 in the Snooker World Championships?
16. Who was the first man to score his 100th first-class century in a Test match?
17. Which team won the first Superbowl?
18. Which football team were the first to win the World Cup twice?
19. Which man became the first person to win five Tour de France titles?
20. John Amechi became the first Brit to do what in America?
21. Lee Germon captained which country in his first cricket Test?
22. Liverpool won the European Cup for the first time in which year?
23. Who was the first black woman to win the Wimbledon singles title?
24. The inaugural World Athletics Championships were held where?
25. In 1958 which football club became the first to have undersoil heating?

GOALIES 1

1. Liverpool bought David James from which club?
2. Who spent thirteen years at Spurs before going to Arsenal for £45,000?
3. Which famous Spanish crooner stopped being a goalkeeper because of a bad injury?
4. Name the Polish goalkeeper who ended England's World Cup dreams at Wembley in 1973?
5. Ian Wright was Best Man at Peter Schmeichel's wedding. True or false?
6. In 'Escape to Victory' which actor played the goalie?
7. What club did England's 1966 World Cup winning goalkeeper play for?
8. Which advert of 1998 had a goalie refusing to play unless he found his teddy?
9. When Maradona performed his 'Hand of God' trick, which goalkeeper did he beat?
10. Who was the England great who lost an eye in a car crash?
11. Mark Bosnich is what nationality?
12. Which goalkeeper saved Carlisle from non-league obscurity with the final kick of the 1998-9 season?
13. What was David Seaman's club before he joined Arsenal?
14. Which goalie was nicknamed Jessie James whilst at Liverpool because: "One shot and you're dead"?
15. In the 1994 World Cup, which Mexican goalkeeper wore hideous outfits?
16. Who was the goalie and captain of Italy's 1982 World Cup winning side?
17. In 1998 which goalkeeper advertised Danepak?
18. Which goalie did Nayim beat from the half-way line in the Cup Winners' Cup final?
19. Which goalie did David Beckham beat from the half-way line?
20. When Preston played Bury in a league game in 1990, what was unusual about it?
21. Which ex-Arsenal goalie is David Seaman's coach?
22. In the 1970 World Cup, who replaced Gordon Banks for the quarter-final against West Germany?
23. Adoni Zubizaretta is a famous goalkeeper from which country?
24. Which Scotland goalie left the France '98 squad following revelations in the newspapers?
25. Which England International was originally a deckchair assistant in Skegness?

Answers to BOXING 2

1. Three Rounds *2.* Kid Galahad *3.* True *4.* Roy Jones *5.* Three Minutes *6.* Don King *7.* No *8.* A person who can box Orthodox or Southpaw *9.* Henry Armstrong *10.* Sugar Ray Robinson *11.* Attempting to lose weight quickly so you can make your limit *12.* Lightweight *13.* Randolph Turpin *14.* Thomas Hearns *15.* Panama *16.* Sugar Ray Leonard *17.* Jake La Motta *18.* One minute *19.* 135lb *20.* Rocky Graciano *21.* Carl Thompson *22.* Win Three successive British title fights at the same weight *23.* America *24.* Cruiserweight *25.* False

MEN'S TENNIS

1. How old was Bjorn Borg when he retired in 1983?
2. What nationality is the tennis player Marcello Rios?
3. Who won the 1998 Australian Open?
4. In which year did Fred Perry last win the Wimbledon Men's Singles title?
5. Ivan Lendl won Wimbledon once. True or false?
6. Boris Becker first won Wimbledon at what age?
7. Was John McEnroe left or right handed?
8. What nationality was Ilie Nastase?
9. Who won the gold at the 1992 Olympics?
10. Who is known as 'Pistol Pete'?
11. In 1990 who retired from the Australian Open final?
12. Who was the first Dutchman to win Wimbledon?
13. Which tennis player hated playing on Thursday 12th of any month because as a child he had crashed his bike into a tree on that day?
14. Which famous tennis player had a superstition of not shaving four days before a major championship?
15. Aces are common in men's tennis. What is an ace?
16. Who was John McEnroe's tennis-playing brother?
17. The 'Voice of Tennis' was the nickname of Dan who?
18. Which tennis star had the nickname 'Muscles'?
19. Who won the Wimbledon Men's Singles title from 1934 to 1936?
20. Which man won his first Wimbledon singles title in 1981?
21. Which Swedish tennis star was born on 6th June 1956?
22. Which British man lost in the 1997 US Open final?
23. How often is the Davis Cup contested?
24. Pat Cash sang a song called 'Rock 'n' Roll' with which other famous player?
25. Bjorn Borg was the first man to win 100 tournaments. True or false?

MIXED BAG 12

1. Tony Drago is a snooker professional from which country?
2. True or false? On the Monopoly Board for France '98, the country representing Old Kent Road was Scotland?
3. What nationality is Pat Cash?
4. The Super 12 is a competition in which sport?
5. Which cricket team has won the most County Championships?
6. The Pamplona Bull Run occurs in which country?
7. In football who are the 'Dons'?
8. Which track is used for the Belgian Grand Prix?
9. In American Football who or what is the QB?
10. Which Argentine driver won the Formula One World Championship for the first time in 1951?
11. Which crew sank in the 1978 boat race?
12. Where will the 2004 Olympics be held?
13. Where do the Expos baseball team come from?
14. Which boxer had the nickname 'Marvellous'?
15. Who were the last Scottish League club to install floodlights in June 1981?
16. Chanda Rubin is an American woman who plays which sport?
17. Who was the captain of England during the Bodyline Series?
18. Kevin Keegan joined Liverpool from which club in 1971?
19. The comedian Nick Hancock supports which football team?
20. Who became England Test cricket captain after Michael Atherton?
21. What does WBC stand for in boxing?
22. What is an Epée used in?
23. Which football team plays at Meadow Lane?
24. Whose name was shortened to Flo-Jo?
25. Which footballer is known as 'Juke Box'?

RECORDS

1. In 1997 Seb Coe's 800 metre World record was finally broken after 16 years. Who broke it?
2. At which Olympics did Bob Beamon perform his amazing long jump record?
3. Before Ian Wright, who was Arsenal's top scorer?
4. Who drove Thrust SSC into the record books in '97?
5. Of the 92 clubs in the English Football League, which player holds the record for scoring the most goals for one club, in total 377?
6. In 1938 who scored a record 364 against Australia?
7. Which man bowled Don Bradman for a duck in his last Test, thus denying him a batting average of over 100?
8. Galina Zabina was a record holder in the 1950's in which sport?
9. What record does Cal Ripken hold in baseball?
10. Who were Roger Bannister's pacemakers when he broke the four minute mile?
11. Which World record holder was expelled from the American Athletics Union for refusing to compete on a Swedish tour, which forced him to make his living running against horses and motorbikes?
12. Name the England cricketer who holds the record of taking 49 wickets in a Test Series?
13. Who holds Manchester United's club goalscoring record?
14. Vasily Alexeyev set over 80 World Records in which sport?
15. In 1998 who scored 34 off one Alex Tudor over?
16. Which was the first English football club to sign three million-pound players?
17. 1 minute 41.73 seconds was whose 800m World record?
18. Which Welshman won the 1984 Chicago Marathon in a record time?
19. Ann Packer set a World record time of 2.01.1 for the 800m at which Olympics?
20. Which famous Kenyan, born in 1952, once held the record for the 3,000m flat, the 3,000m Steeplechase, the 5,000m and the 10,000m?
21. Donald and Malcolm were father and son who held land and water speed records. What was their surname?
22. Who was the Champion Jockey an amazing 26 times in this country?
23. Gary Sobers hit six sixes off which Glamorgan bowler?
24. In 1961 Roger Maris set a record of 61 what in a season?
25. How old was Dick Saunders when he won the Grand National in 1982 on Grittar: 48, 49 or 50?

CAPTAINS

1. Who was the captain of the losing 1999 Ryder Cup team?
2. Who captained Scotland when they beat England 1-0 at Wembley in the Euro 2000 play-offs?
3. Which former England rugby union captain was jailed for five years in 1998?
4. Douglas Jardine was England captain during the 'Bodyline Series'. In which country was he born?
5. Which man played for Liverpool, Wolves and England as well as captaining a team on 'A Question of Sport'?
6. Which actor played the leader and captain of the POW's in the film 'Escape to Victory'?
7. When the British Lions toured South Africa in 1997, who was the captain?
8. When Spurs won the League and Cup double in '61, who was the skipper?
9. In which year did Michael Atherton first captain England?
10. Which Middlesbrough manager was called 'Captain Courageous'?
11. Who was the winning captain of the Ryder Cup in 1997?
12. Which England cricket captain was offered the throne of Albania?
13. Who was the captain of the 1997-98 Premiership winners?
14. Who led the England cricket team before Graham Gooch?
15. What did Captain Matthew Webb do in 1875 that had never been done before?
16. Which England football captain was accused of stealing a bracelet while in Columbia?
17. Who captained the England football team 90 times from 1948?
18. Who was Brazil's captain at France '98?
19. Rachael Heyhoe-Flint captained England at cricket but at what other sport did she represent her country?
20. Who captained the winners of France '98?
21. Which New Zealand cricket captain wrote the book 'Hell of a way to earn a living'?
22. Tony Jacklin captained the Ryder Cup team four times but how many victories did he enjoy in this role?
23. In rugby union, who captained the first team to win the World Cup?
24. Which man replaced Alec Stewart as England cricket captain?
25. Why is Captain Keith Brown famous?

REFEREES
AND UMPIRES

1. In 1987 which England cricketer had a row with the umpire in the Lahore Test?
2. Referee Peter Willis did what for the first time in the 1985 FA Cup final?
3. John Anderson is the referee associated with which TV show?
4. Mills Lane is a well-known referee from which sport?
5. In football they used to be called linesmen. What are they now called?
6. Who was the Premiership's first black referee?
7. What does cricket umpire David Shepherd do when the score reaches 'Nelson'?
8. In 1998 Mike Tyson was paid $4 Million to referee which sport?
9. If the ref was the 'Fatman' and the two competitors were the 'Viking' and the 'Count', what would the sport be?
10. Mike Sweeney was the umpire of which event on 28th March 1998?
11. In American Football the referee has the nickname 'Zebra'. True or false?
12. In 1964 what did lineswoman Dorothy Brown do at Wimbledon that caught the headlines?
13. How many umpires referee an Aussie Rules game: 4, 6 or 10?
14. Roberto Alomar caused outrage and almost started an umpires' strike when he spat at an umpire in which sport?
15. Which referee sent off David Beckham in France '98?
16. Staying with France '98, what nationality was the referee in the final?
17. If an umpire raises both arms above his head in a game of cricket what does it mean?
18. You don't have linesmen in rugby union. What are they called instead?
19. What is a Gyoji?
20. Which famous umpire was born on 19th April 1933?
21. Which tennis player said this to a policeman: "You must arrest him, he's the worst umpire I've ever seen"?
22. Which Leicester player was banned after pushing the referee at the end of the rugby union Pilkington Cup final in 1996?
23. Peter Willey is an official in which sport?
24. Catherine McTavish was the first female umpire at which Grand Slam Tennis Tournament?
25. At Old Trafford in 1981, Dennis Lillee and Rodney Marsh put a rubber snake in which umpire's soup?

CHEATS, DODGY RESULTS AND MISBEHAVIOUR

1. Which American State made golf cheating punishable by a 5-year prison sentence in 1974?
2. In 1978 Argentina defeated which team 6-0 in the World Cup?
3. Following on from that, where was Peru's goalkeeper from?
4. Maradona used his 'Hand of God' excuse at which World Cup?
5. Boris Onishenko rigged his epée to record non-existent hits at which Olympics?
6. When Ali fought Cooper, his glove was split by his manager. What was his name?
7. Name the European golfer who had his line trampled all over by the American team celebrating a putt at the end of the 1999 Ryder Cup?
8. Dora Ratjen won the Olympic High Jump in the 1936 Olympics but why was her medal later taken away?
9. Norbert Sudhaus won the 1972 Olympic Marathon. How did he cheat?
10. What did Tonya Harding have done to Nancy Kerrigan in an attempt to win a Gold Medal?
11. With reference to the 1972 Olympics, what do Americans mean by the 'big lie' ?
12. Why was Kathy Jager accused of cheating at the 1999 World Veteran Athletics Championships?
13. In which sport is 'Sledging' a term for putting your opponent off their game?
14. Which man made a questionable move at Adelaide in the 90's that in turn stopped Damon Hill winning the Formula 1 Championship?
15. Lester Piggott was jailed for tax evasion in which year?
16. Jack Dempsey lost to whom in 1927 in "The battle of the long count"?
17. In 1930 who was disqualified in a World Heavyweight Title fight?
18. Which baseball team deliberately lost the 1919 World Series?
19. In 1981 New Zealand needed 6 runs of the last ball against Australia. What happened next?
20. Ian Botham lost a libel case after which former Pakistan captain called him a cheat?
21. Which Irish woman won three gold medals at the Atlanta Olympics?
22. In horse racing what is a 'ringer'?
23. Tony Kay and Peter Swan were England Internationals jailed in the 60's for trying to fix matches in which sport?
24. Roberto Rojas was a goalie who faked injury from a flare during a World Cup qualifying match against Brazil. He was subsequently banned for life. Which country did he represent?
25. In which athletic event can you be disqualified for 'lifting'?

MIXED BAG 13

1. Bernie Ecclestone is a name from which sport?
2. In squash what does ESRF stand for?
3. Coventry won the FA Cup in 1987 by beating which team in the final?
4. In rugby union, how many points do you get for a converted try?
5. Which football team does Tony Blair support?
6. Where do the Baltimore Orioles play their home games?
7. Which Swedish driver died at Monza in 1978?
8. Highfield Road is the home of which football club?
9. Which Yorkshire club won the last First Division Championship in 1992?
10. Joe Frazier won his heavyweight gold at which Olympics?
11. Which country has a tennis open played at a place called Bastad?
12. Which man played in the first six World Cup Cricket Tournaments?
13. How many team members are there in the Ryder Cup team?
14. Nelson who won the Formula One World Championship three times in the 80's?
15. Which England fast bowler of the 1950's was known as 'Typhoon'?
16. Anfield is the former ground of Everton. True or false?
17. Minnesota Fats is a name associated with which sport?
18. How many goals did Bobby Charlton score for England?
19. 'Hands of Stone' was the nickname of which boxer?
20. Name the older of the cricket-playing Hollioake brothers?
21. The King George VI and Queen Elizabeth II Diamond Stakes are held at which racecourse?
22. Name the footballer sometimes referred to as 'Duncan Disorderly'?
23. Estoril is the track for which Grand Prix?
24. A hooker normally has which number on his back in a game of rugby union?
25. As of the summer of 1999 who is credited with bowling the fastest ever ball in cricket?

MONEY

1. How much did Newcastle Utd pay for Alan Shearer?
2. By qualifying for the 1982 World Cup which team received £6000, a car and a house each?
3. Which city got itself into big financial trouble by holding the Olympics in 1976?
4. Which Man City chairman made his money from toilet rolls?
5. Which Arsenal manager was sacked following 'bung' allegations?
6. If you bet a 'Lady Godiva' what would be your stake?
7. Which football hero was once asked: "Where did it all go wrong?" as he reclined on a bed of money with Miss World?
8. What odds are described as a hand?
9. Which football club does Doug Ellis own?
10. George II put a £10 levy on every public house that had what type of table?
11. Which Rupert invested in rugby league to turn it into Super League?
12. Sheik Mohammed Al Maktoum is a name associated with which sport?
13. Which Norwegian skater made her fortune in Hollywood having won three Olympic golds?
14. Which Lloyd has his own fitness and tennis empire?
15. Bernie Ecclestone gave the press a field day in 1998 when he donated large sum of money to which political party?
16. Glenn Hoddle sold his World Cup Diaries in a serialisation to which tabloid paper?
17. In 1994, which sport went on strike when the players asked for more money from the owners?
18. The Arlington Million is a horse race in which country?
19. Paul Newlove left which club for £500,000 to join St Helens?
20. Which commentator, known for his chin, was instrumental in the abolition of the maximum wage for footballers?
21. Who in 1988 was the subject of the first £2,000,000 transfer between two British clubs?
22. In 1998, which Man Utd player became the world's most expensive defender?
23. Which female golfer is said to have blown $500,000 at the poker table?
24. 'Hey Big Spender' is a fanzine devoted to which football club?
25. Walt Disney did a film called 'The Happiest Millionaire'. Which sport was it about?

SWIMMING

1. Mark Spitz was talking about which facial feature when he said: "It acts as a kind of shield, the water slides off it and I can go faster"?
2. How many golds did Irish swimmer Michelle Smith win at the Atlanta Olympics?
3. What nationality is Michael Klim?
4. Who, in 1875, became the first person swim the English Channel?
5. Which man was stabbed in the back in Moscow in 1996?
6. Duncan Goodhew won Olympic gold in which event?
7. In 1998 four coaches from which country went to court after giving performance enhancing steroids to swimmers between 1975 and 1989?
8. At the Seoul Olympics, which American man won the most swimming medals?
9. Who is the 'Albatross'?
10. In 1987 who became the first man to break a minute for a 100m Breaststroke in a 25m pool?
11. Which British swimmer won the men's 1500m bronze at the Atlanta Games?
12. Captain Matthew Webb died attempting to swim which natural phenomenom?
13. Which woman won three successive Olympic golds for the 100m freestyle in 1956, 1960 and 1964?
14. Which swimmer lost his hair after he fell out of a tree aged 10?
15. Who was the swimming great who became a dentist in Southern California?
16. The shortest competitive distance in swimming is 100m. True or false?
17. Name all four Olympic swimming strokes?
18. In metres, how long is an Olympic size pool?
19. Which British swimmer used to date the judo star Neil Adams?
20. Who was the first person to swim 100m in under a minute?
21. Kristin Otto won six gold medals at which Olympics?
22. Gertrude Ederle was the first woman to swim what in 1926?
23. John Hencken set 12 World records between 1972 and 1976 in which stroke?
24. Which female Australian swimmer won three golds at the 1972 Olympics and then retired in 1973 aged 16?
25. Harry Hebner is credited with changing which stroke to what we know today?

SPANISH SPORT

1. How many times did Miguel Indurain win the Tour De France?
2. Carlos Moya is a name associated with which sport?
3. How old was Arantxa Sanchez when she won the French Open in 1989?
4. Englishman Henry Higgins was a hero in Spain for doing what?
5. In which year did Spain host the Football World Cup?
6. Which Spanish tennis player won the men's French Open in 1998?
7. Which infamous owner of Atletico Madrid sacked Ron Atkinson while his team were top of the Spanish league?
8. What sport do the Barcelona Dragons play?
9. Which World Heavyweight Champion became a Matador whilst in Europe?
10. Which Spanish club sacked John Toshack for the second time in 1999?
11. Who was the first British footballer in this country to be transferred for a fee of £2,000,000?
12. Who was the only player to be part of each of Real Madrid's first six European Cup winning teams?
13. Estadio Santiago Bernabeu is the full name of which football team's home ground?
14. The 'Vuelta D'Espana' was first held in 1935. What is the sport?
15. Which fast ball game involves players catching and throwing a ball with a basket like glove against a wall?
16. Who was the first Spanish captain of the European Ryder Cup team?
17. What football position does Adoni Zubizarreta play?
18. Which Spanish golfer is known as 'El Nino'?
19. From which English football team did Athletico Bilbao get their home strip?
20. Which British cyclist finished third behind Abraham Olano and Miguel Indurain in the 1996 Olympic Road Race?
21. Which Spanish defender is known as the 'Beast'?
22. Which team missed a vital penalty in the last minute of their last game of the 1996 season, to hand the title to Barcelona?
23. Which Spaniard triumphed at the 1999 US Masters?
24. In which year did Spain win the European Football Championship: 1960, 1964 or 1968?
25. Which Spanish striker was known as the 'vulture'?

MIXED BAG 14

1. What nationality was Evonne Goolagong?
2. In a game of rugby union, which position conventionally puts the ball into the scrum?
3. Was Jimmy Connors left or right handed?
4. Who was boxing's first black World Heavyweight Champion?
5. In a game of tiddlywinks, what name is given to the large disc?
6. Following on from that, what is the small disc called?
7. Where have Charlton Athletic traditionally played their home games?
8. How many times has Virginia Wade won the Wimbledon singles title?
9. Who was the first captain to take ten wickets and score a century in the same Test match?
10. Which Italian club did Gazza turn out for?
11. 'The Louisville Lip' was the tag given to which boxer?
12. Commentator Ian Robertson played rugby for which country?
13. Which flat racing Classic is run over a distance of 1 mile 6 furlongs 127 yards?
14. Which famous author of 'Patriot Games' would you associate with the Baltimore Orioles?
15. The Vikings come from where in American Football?
16. Dion Dublin played for which football team before Coventry City?
17. By winning the World Snooker Championship in 1998, who knocked Stephen Hendry off the No1 spot?
18. Tom Courtenay and James Bolam both starred in which film about distance running?
19. In basketball who is Sir Charles?
20. You sit in a Canadian canoe. True or false?
21. Anton Geesink was a world-beater in which sport?
22. Ajax come from which Dutch City?
23. Godfrey Rampling won Gold in the 1936 Olympics but what's the name of his more famous daughter?
24. Which woman won the Wimbledon singles title for the last time in 1975?
25. Who was the 'Ambling Alp'?

WELSH SPORT

1. Who defeated Wales 51-0 in the 1998 Five Nations Championship?
2. Wimbledon bought John Hartson from which club?
3. Who is Ryan Wilson better known as?
4. Which famous winger represented Wales at the 1970 Commonwealth Games as a sprinter?
5. Iwan Thomas runs which athletic distance?
6. Gareth Edwards first captained his country at what age?
7. Which Welsh rugby player was a semi-finalist in the 110m hurdles at the 1984 Olympics?
8. How many Five Nations Grand Slams did Wales win in the 80's?
9. Which Welshman scored a last minute try at Wembley to deny England the 1999 Five Nations Championship?
10. The Cardiff Devils play which sport?
11. Which Snooker player said: "I can't remember anyone ever asking who came second, can you"?
12. Who is the hurdler well known for loving chocolate?
13. Name the fly-half who played rugby league for Widnes and Warrington before going back to rugby union?
14. In which rugby position does Robert Howley play?
15. Who was 'Merv the Swerve'?
16. 'Gosh it's Tosh' was a book of poems by which Welsh striker?
17. Tony Lewis commentates on which sport?
18. Which man won the long jump gold at the 1964 Olympics?
19. Who was the 1978 World Darts Champion?
20. Which boxer never recovered from a coma after losing to Lupe Pintor in 1980?
21. 'The Mighty Atom' was the nickname of which boxer?
22. The Racecourse Ground is the home of which football team?
23. Which Welsh golfer was born on 2nd March 1958?
24. Wales played their first International football match in 1876, losing 4 - 0 to which country?
25. Name the Irish boxer who was supposed to fight Joe Calzaghe just before he retired?

WINTER SPORTS AND OLYMPICS

1. The Cresta Run can be found in which resort?
2. Where did the Winter Olympics of 1998 take place?
3. Robert Redford and Gene Hackman star in which film about a downhill racer?
4. Calgary, then Albertville. Where was next?
5. There is only one event measured to one-thousandth of a second at the Winter games. What is it?
6. Betty Callaway coached which famous duo?
7. How many medals did Britain win at the 1998 games?
8. In which sport do you go 'into the house'?
9. What nationality was the famous skier Franz Klammer?
10. 'Cool Runnings' was a film based on events at which Winter Olympics?
11. In which country were the first Winter Olympics held?
12. Ski jumping originates from which country?
13. Which World and Olympic skating champion died in 1995 aged 28 at Lake Placid following an accident in training?
14. In figure skating, how long is the short program?
15. Why did they have a Winter Olympics in 1994 after there had been one in 1992?
16. What was Christopher Dean's job before becoming an ice skater?
17. Tara Lipinski is a figure skating champ from which country?
18. What is the NISA in Britain?
19. What is the biathlon a combination of?
20. In which event do you have a 'halfpipe'?
21. Kirsty Hay represented Great Britain at Nagano in which event?
22. The Austrian skier Herman Maier has a nickname what is it?
23. When was snowboarding first introduced as a Winter Olympic sport?
24. The Art Ross Trophy is awarded in which icy sport?
25. What was Charles Jewlraw the first to do?

COMMONWEALTH GAMES

1. Where will the 2002 Games be held?
2. Barry McGuigan won a boxing gold at which weight?
3. Before the 1998 Games which British woman had won medals at five successive games?
4. Which city hosted the Games in 1970 and 1986?
5. Which Englishman won gold medals in bowls in 1962, 1970, 1974 and 1978?
6. Who was Reverend J Atley Cooper?
7. Where did the first Games take place?
8. In 1982 Alan Wells and Mike McFarlane ran a dead heat in which event?
9. What were the Commonwealth Games originally called?
10. Chris Sheasby was selected for England at which event in 1998?
11. Precious McKenzie won numerous Commonwealth medals in which sport?
12. Where were the 1998 Commonwealth Games held?
13. Gillian Clark won 12 medals, of which six were golds, in which sport?
14. Keith Connor won two golds for which country at the triple jump?
15. In which year of the 1930's were the Games first held?
16. Which future boxing World Champion won the Middleweight gold in 1970?
17. Name the well-known female Scottish runner who won the 10,000m at the 1986 games?
18. Kathy who won seven medals for England in the sprints in the 70's and 80's?
19. How many rounds are there in a Commonwealth boxing bout?
20. Cricket took place for the first time at the 1998 Games. True or false?
21. How often are the Commonwealth Games held?
22. At which Games did athletics go metric?
23. Did women compete at the first Commonwealth Games?
24. Which football team will get a new stadium after the 2002 Games?
25. Which island held the Games in 1966?

MIXED BAG 15

1. Gillian Gilks is a name associated with which sport?
2. Which football team plays at Ewood Park?
3. How many points is the brown ball worth in snooker?
4. The women's horse vault is the same height as the men's. True or false?
5. In football who are 'The Gunners'?
6. If you hit a golf ball 'fat' what does it mean?
7. The Hickstead Derby is in which sport?
8. 'The Motor City Cobra' was the nickname of which boxer?
9. How many times did Alain Prost win the World Drivers Championship in the 80's?
10. In professional boxing which weight is above lightweight?
11. Who were the skaters involved in the 'Battle of Wounded Knee'?
12. On the France '98 Monopoly board which team represented Mayfair?
13. Telekom is a cycling team from which country?
14. Which retired British sprinter was sometimes called the 'Lunchbox'?
15. Before a try was worth five points in rugby union how points was it worth?
16. When a quarterback is tackled behind the line of scrimmage what is this called?
17. Sydney Marie was a runner who left South Africa and represented which other country at the Olympics?
18. Frank Bruno won a World Heavyweight Title at what attempt?
19. Who won the Ryder Cup in 1987?
20. Which Grand Prix champion was born in Melbourne in 1946?
21. Babe Ruth retired from baseball in which decade?
22. When a horse is described as 'dead meat' what does it mean?
23. Which football team used to be called St Domingo's?
24. In the decathlon is the pole vault on the first or second day?
25. Which agent is known for saying 'monster' a lot?

A CENTURY OF SPORT –
1900-1929

1. Who became World Boxing Champion in 1908?
2. Anthony Wilding won Wimbledon between 1910 and 1913. What was his nationality?
3. Where were the 1928 Winter Olympics held?
4. In which year did the first Greyhound Derby take place?
5. The Summer Olympics of 1924 took place in which city?
6. Who scored 60 goals in the 1927-28 season in the English First Division?
7. The 1912 FA Cup final took place at which ground?
8. Which man took 17 South African wickets in a single Test?
9. In 1928 which home nation thrashed England 5-1 at Wembley?
10. Man Utd moved to Old Trafford in which year: 1908, 1910 or 1912?
11. What nationality was the golfer Walter Hagen?
12. Which monarch owned the 1909 Derby winner?
13. Who lost his World heavyweight boxing title in 1915?
14. USA won 244 of a potential 281 medals at which Olympics?
15. In 1907 which Scottish football team became the first to do the double?
16. When Wynham Halswelle won the 400m at the 1908 Olympics what was different about the race?
17. In 1923 which stadium was tagged 'The House that Ruth Built'?
18. The first British Grand Prix took place in 1926 at which track?
19. Who won the World Snooker Championships in 1927 and remained champion until 1947?
20. France built which tennis stadium in the west of Paris in 1928?
21. Which FA Cup final is called the 'White Horse' final?
22. In 1928 which country became the fourth Test cricket side?
23. May Sutton became the first woman from overseas to win what in 1905?
24. What was formed in 1907 at the Imperial Hotel, Manchester with Billy Meredith as chairman?
25. Abraham Saperstein founded which famous basketball team in 1927?

A CENTURY OF SPORT – 1930-1939

1. The Summer Olympics took place in which city in 1936?
2. Which team lost in the 1930 World Cup final?
3. Who beat Primo Carrera in 1934 to become World Heavyweight Champion?
4. In which year did Lake Placid host the Winter Olympics?
5. Joe Louis beat whom to become World Heavyweight Champion?
6. In 1933 Everton played Man City in the FA Cup final. What was different about this final?
7. Which terminally ill baseball player said at the Yankees stadium in 1939: "I may have been given a bad break... but I consider myself the luckiest man on earth"?
8. Who set a world long jump record of 8.13m in 1935 which stood for 25 years?
9. Which English cricketer scored a then World record 364 in 1938 against Australia?
10. Who won the English First Division five times this decade?
11. Which golfer was known as the 'Iceman' and the 'Killer'?
12. How many teams competed in the first World Cup in 1930: 11,13 or 15?
13. Name the Welshman who fought Joe Louis in 1937?
14. Who was known as the 'Cinderella Man'?
15. In the Bodyline series who was the main England bowler who pinned down the Aussie batsmen?
16. Which of the countries who make up the Five Nations rugby tournament did the others ban in the 30's?
17. Bruce Hobbs won the Grand National on a horse called **Battleship**, making him the youngest jockey to win the race. How old was he?
18. When was the first televised FA Cup final?
19. Which Moody woman won her eighth Wimbledon Singles title in 1938?
20. Which boxer was called 'Homicide Hank'?
21. The 1939 timeless Test between England and South Africa was abandoned when England had to board the ship home. How many days did the Test last?
22. At the 1938 World Cup, the better Austrian players were picked to play for which other country?
23. How many gold medals did Jesse Owens win at the 1936 Olympics?
24. Don Bradman has held the record for scoring the most runs in a Test series since 1930. How many runs did he make in that series?
25. In 1938 Stanley Matthews asked for a transfer from his then club, but stayed there until he was 47. Which club?

A CENTURY OF SPORT – 1940-1949

1. The Summer Olympics of 1944 were cancelled due to war. Where were they due to be held?
2. Jackie Robinson became the first black man to play Major League baseball. Which team signed him?
3. How many times were the Winter Olympics held in this decade?
4. Which future heavyweight champion attempted to play professional baseball for the Chicago Cubs in 1947?
5. How many football World Cup finals took place in the 40's?
6. Jimmy Doyle died in a World Welterweight Championship bout after losing to which boxing great?
7. Who scored 208 for England against South Africa at Lords in 1947?
8. In which year was Rocky Marciano's first professional fight: 1947, 1948 or 1949?
9. Who became manager of Manchester United in 1945?
10. In which year did Don Bradman retire from Test cricket?
11. Which female athlete was the sensation of the 1948 Olympics?
12. Which country won the first-ever World Volleyball Championships?
13. In American Football, the Rams moved from Cleveland to which other American city?
14. Mahmoud Kerim won the British Open in 1946 the first time he entered. What was the sport?
15. Which boxing legend won the Welterweight title in 1946?
16. 'Slammin' Sam' was a nickname for which golfer?
17. Leslie Graham won the world's first 500cc Championship in which year?
18. In 1949 which Scottish football team did the treble?
19. Which World Heavyweight Champion announced his retirement on 1st March 1949?
20. Brian Bevan joined which Cheshire rugby league club in 1945?
21. Keith Miller was an outstanding cricketer for which Test Side?
22. Frank Miller captained the England football team from which position?
23. In 1949 which Italian football champions were involved in a crash, killing all 17 passengers?
24. Peter Gray played for the St Louis Browns 77 times with only one what?
25. Don Bradman scored a double century in his last Test match. True or false?

A CENTURY OF SPORT – 1950-1959

1. The first BBC Sports Personality of the Year was Chris Chataway in which year?
2. Who was the World Heavyweight Champion after Joe Louis?
3. Johnny Leach was a World Champion in which sport in 1951?
4. Which man took 19 wickets for 90 runs at Old Trafford in 1956?
5. What was Roger Bannister's race number when he broke the 4-minute mile?
6. Where did the Summer Olympics of 1952 take place?
7. Which horse seemed certain to win the 1956 Grand National, yet failed in sight of the winning post?
8. Emil Zatopek won three golds at the 1952 games at which events?
9. In 1955 which man played football for England aged just 18?
10. What was the venue for the 1956 Winter Olympic games?
11. Which Briton was World Motor Racing Champion in 1958?
12. Who became World Heavyweight Champion in 1952?
13. Which man won four 500cc world titles in the 50's?
14. Who sank in the 1951 boat race?
15. Which jockey rode his first Derby winner in 1953 on Pinza?
16. The first World Grand Prix Championship was held in which year in this decade?
17. Twins Di and Ros Rowe were both World Champions in which sport?
18. Which former England cricket captain was knighted in 1954?
19. Billy Boston is a fifties name from which sport?
20. Who won the FA Cup most times this decade?
21. In which year was the Munich air disaster?
22. Who, in 1959, became the first footballer to play 100 times for his country?
23. How old was Floyd Patterson when he became World Heavyweight champion?
24. Rocky Marciano's last professional fight was against whom in 1955?
25. In 1954, who became the youngest person to win the Derby?

A CENTURY OF SPORT – 1960-1969

1. Which two teams contested the Battle of Santiago during the 1962 World Cup in which players pucnhed and kicked each other?
2. Which Brazilian woman won Wimbledon in 1960 and 1964?
3. England won the World Cup on which date?
4. Who, in 1962, was the first woman to win the BBC Sports Personality of the Year?
5. Who became the World Heavyweight Champion in 1962 after beating Floyd Patterson?
6. Beryl Burton was a World Champion at which sport in the 1960's?
7. Who was Man Utd's captain when they won the European Cup?
8. What nationality was the Leeds Utd winger Albert Johannson?
9. The 1964 Summer Olympics took place in which Asian city?
10. Who became Man Utd manager after Matt Busby in 1969?
11. In which year this decade did the first Superbowl take place?
12. Which Belgian won the Tour de France in 1969?
13. Joe Namath was the quarterback of which winning Superbowl team in 1969?
14. How many teams entered the 1966 World Cup?
15. Age Hadler was a Norwegian who became the first men's World Champion in which sport?
16. Martin Peters was the first £200,000 footballer when he moved from West Ham to which club, with Jimmy Greaves going the other way?
17. Which team won the English First Division in 1968?
18. Which country hosted the World Cup in 1962, when Brazil won it?
19. How many times did Rod Laver win the Wimbledon singles title this decade?
20. Which showjumper was BBC Sports Personality of the Year in 1960?
21. Where were the 1960 Winter Olympics held?
22. Who, from 1962, became the first man to win four successive World 500cc titles?
23. Which West Indies cricket captain was knighted in 1964?
24. In 1961 which Fulham player became the first £100 a week footballer in this country?
25. Which famous football team were forced to resign from the Football League on 6th March 1962?

A CENTURY OF SPORT – 1970-1979

1. In the last game of the 1973-74 football season, Denis Law scored a goal for Man City. Why didn't he celebrate it?
2. How many times did the West Indies win the Cricket World Cup in this decade?
3. Which goalkeeper made an amazing save from Pele's bouncing header in the 1970 World Cup?
4. Red Rum won the Grand National for the first time in which year?
5. The 1978 World Cup was held in which country?
6. In which year did the Football League change the way it separated teams level on points from goal average to goal difference?
7. Who hosted 'World of Sport' throughout the 70's?
8. What was the most-watched live sport on British television in the 1970's?
9. In 1978 who was the first black footballer to play for England at senior level?
10. Which cricketer scored 174 in Melbourne in the Centenary Test?
11. Who won the FA Cup most times this decade?
12. In 1976, who became the first Briton to win an Olympic gold in swimming for 68 years?
13. Mary Peters won the pentathlon gold medal at which Olympics?
14. Virginia Wade won the Wimbledon title in 1977 beating whom in the final?
15. Who hosted the World Cup in 1974?
16. When the British Lions toured New Zealand in 1971 who was the captain?
17. How many times did Bjorn Borg win the Wimbledon Men's Singles title this decade?
18. 1976 saw the Winter Olympics held at which location?
19. Which horse won the Cheltenham Gold Cup in 1970 and 1971?
20. Who won the WBA Heavyweight Title in 1978 after beating Ken Norton?
21. The first one-day cricket International took place in 1971 between which two countries?
22. Name the double World Formula One champion who died in 1975 in a plane crash?
23. Who won the World Snooker Championship in 1978 aged 45?
24. Which Welsh BBC commentator described Gareth Edwards' famous try, playing for the Barbarians in 1973 against New Zealand?
25. Which former World heavyweight was found dead on 30th December 1970?

A CENTURY OF SPORT – 1980-1989

1. Who lost in three FA Cup finals in the 80's?
2. How many times did Steve Davis become World Snooker champion?
3. Which woman won the London Marathon four times this decade?
4. When Shergar won the Derby in 1981 who was the jockey?
5. Silvino Francisco was a name in the 1980's in which sport?
6. Why was Lester Piggott sent to jail?
7. Larry Holmes beat Ali in which year?
8. Controversially, Britain gave which female athlete a British passport so she could run and bolster our 1984 Olympic team?
9. Which streaker released a single called 'Remember Then'?
10. Who was the darts player described as 'fat, boozy and toothless'?
11. Who won the Wimbledon Men's Singles title in 1982?
12. At which Olympics did Tessa Sanderson win gold in the javelin?
13. How many times did England win the Five Nations rugby championship in this decade?
14. Which well-known TV programme, hosted by David Vine, was axed by the BBC in 1985?
15. Who won the old English First Division in the last minute of the last game of the 1989 season?
16. John McEnroe won the Wimbledon Men's Singles title for the last time in which year: 1983, 84 or 85?
17. In 1980 the Winter Olympics was held at which calm venue?
18. Which famous horse won the Cheltenham Gold Cup in 1989?
19. In 1986 which batsman scored the then fastest-ever Test century on his home ground in Antigua?
20. Which darts player became the first in his sport to receive an MBE in 1989?
21. Who became the first Briton to win the Women's US Golf Open?
22. Which management great died as he watched Scotland play Wales at Ninian Park?
23. Who did New Zealand beat 108-4 in a 1987 rugby union International?
24. In 1988 Liverpool bought back Ian Rush from which Italian club?
25. In 1986 who did Wigan buy for a record £100,000 from Widnes?

A CENTURY OF SPORT –
1990. IN THIS YEAR...

1. Who hosted the World Cup?
2. How old was Stephen Hendry when he won the World Snooker Championship?
3. Alec Stewart made his Test debut. True or false?
4. Pete Sampras won the US Open. How old was he?
5. Which golfer won both the British Open and the US Masters?
6. Who won the Five Nations Championship?
7. Which sprinter helped launch a campaign for the Milk Marketing Board?
8. Which 'keeper was dropped for the FA Cup final replay?
9. Arsenal were deducted how many points for fighting?
10. Who was the team they fought?
11. Buster Douglas defeated Mike Tyson in how many rounds?
12. Who was the 100-1 outsider who won the World Professional Darts championship?
13. The Australian Tennis Open expelled which famous tennis player because of his behaviour?
14. The Taylor Report was concerned with the safety of what?
15. Who became the first man to take 400 Test wickets?
16. Who lost in the FA Cup final replay?
17. The World Cup was won by which team?
18. Terry Marsh was charged with the attempted murder of whom, only later to be acquitted?
19. The Cheltenham Gold Cup was won by which outsider?
20. Who became the first golfer to win $6 million on the US PGA Tour?
21. Which batsman scored 333 against India at Lord's?
22. The Formula One World Championship was won by which driver?
23. Who received a 10-month ban from snooker after threatening Dennis Taylor?
24. Gazza cried after getting booked whilst playing against which country?
25. Who became the first British athlete to set a World record at home in 17 years by throwing the javelin 90.98m?

A CENTURY OF SPORT –
1991. IN THIS YEAR...

1. Jet Ski Lad won which Classic horse race priced at 50-1?
2. Which player, aged 15, became the youngest to score a 147 break at the English Amateur Championships?
3. Which woman was BBC Sports Personality of the Year?
4. Which man broke Bob Beamon's World long jump record?
5. When Great Britain won the 4x400m at the World Championships, who where the four men?
6. Who won the British Open?
7. Which university boat race team named their boats Iraq and Rest of the World?
8. Who won the second Rugby World Cup?
9. Who did they beat in the final?
10. The FA Cup was won by?
11. Which German won the Wimbledon Men's Singles title?
12. The US PGA was won by which man after only his third professional tournament?
13. Martin Crowe and Andrew Jones shared a partnership of 467 for New Zealand against which Test side?
14. The European Cup Winners' Cup was won by?
15. Steffi Graf won the Wimbledon Singles title. True or false?
16. Which club sold Mark Wright and Dean Saunders to Liverpool?
17. Who was the famous boxer charged with rape?
18. The Ryder Cup was won by which team?
19. The Ryder Cup took place at which course?
20. Who quit as Liverpool's manager on Febuary 22nd?
21. The Ashes were won by which team?
22. Who was the famous cricketer who flew with John Morris over a cricket ground in a Tiger Moth plane?
23. How Grand Slam tournaments did Monica Seles win?
24. Who became the first Briton to win World boxing titles at two different weights?
25. Michael Watson went into a coma after fighting which boxer?

A CENTURY OF SPORT –
1992. IN THIS YEAR...

1. Sunderland lost to which team in the FA Cup final?
2. Which club won the English First Division?
3. Dan Maskell died aged 84. He was called the voice of which sport?
4. In cricket, which country won the fifth World Cup?
5. Which county signed Ian Botham and Dean Jones?
6. Denmark, who went on to win the European Championships, were a late entry because which team were disqualified?
7. Highbury erected a huge mural of football fans to cover work on the North Bank. What was reported to be wrong with it?
8. Which heavyweight boxer was convicted of rape?
9. Graham Taylor took England to the European Championships. In which country were they held?
10. The losers in cricket's World Cup final were?
11. Nigel Mansell won the Formula One World Championship driving for which team?
12. The Grand National was won by which horse?
13. Where did the Olympic Games take place?
14. The Winter Olympics took place where?
15. Who was the Liverpool manager who had a triple heart by-pass?
16. Which Army town had its football club wound up in March due to debts?
17. The Superbowl was won by?
18. Kevin Keegan became the manager of which club?
19. Who was captain of the Great Britain men's athletics team at the Summer Olympics?
20. Who was the England great banned from receiving FA Cup final tickets, after he was allegedly caught selling them on the black market?
21. Sally Gunnell won a gold medal at the Olympics in which event?
22. The Five Nations rugby championship was won by?
23. The West Indies played South Africa for the very first time in a Test match. Who won the contest?
24. Which British sprinter was sent home from the Olympics?
25. Andre Agassi won the Wimbledon Men's Singles title. True or false?

A CENTURY OF SPORT – 1993. IN THIS YEAR...

1. Which female tennis star was stabbed?
2. Pete Sampras won Wimbledon for the first time. True or false?
3. Lennox Lewis fought whom in his first World Title fight?
4. Who became the first manager to win both the English and Scottish League titles?
5. Brian Clough retired as manager of which club?
6. The 'Fan Man' dropped out of the sky into the boxing ring when a World Heavyweight Title was taking place between Evander Holyfield and which other fighter?
7. Who won the Ryder Cup: USA or Europe?
8. Which team were the first from outside the USA to win baseball's World Series?
9. In November who defeated Stephen Hendry in the UK Open to become the youngest person to win a ranking tournament?
10. Who scored the winning goal for Arsenal in extra time of the FA Cup final replay?
11. Who was the new England cricket captain?
12. Which two fighters contested the first ever all-British Heavyweight World title?
13. What was the venue for this fight?
14. Who was the infamous starter of the Grand National?
15. The Premiership was won by Liverpool. True or false?
16. Who became the youngest man to score 20,000 first-class runs?
17. The British Lions toured which country?
18. Who lost in both the FA Cup and League Cup finals?
19. Where was the Ryder Cup held?
20. Who was the famous tennis player, who died aged 49, who was the first black man to win a Grand Slam tournament?
21. Which city hosted the World Athletics Championships?
22. Who won the Superbowl?
23. Who won the Five Nations Championship?
24. Which England World Cup winning captain died?
25. Who won golf's British Open?

A CENTURY OF SPORT –
1994. IN THIS YEAR...

1. Who collided with Damon Hill, shattering his chance of winning the World title, at the Adelaide Grand Prix?
2. Which famous former Man Utd player was knighted?
3. Oliver McCall defeated whom to become World Heavyweight Champion?
4. Which British athlete won the Men's 400m title at the European Athletics Championships?
5. Which nation hosted the World Cup?
6. Which famous Argentine player was expelled from that World Cup?
7. Who did the English football double?
8. Brian Lara scored 375 against which Test side?
9. Who won the World Series?
10. After 47 days which man quit as the Wales football coach?
11. Ayrton Senna died at which Grand Prix?
12. Which other driver died at the same Grand Prix, during practice?
13. Michael Atherton was caught with what in his pocket?
14. George Foreman became World Heavyweight Champion at what age?
15. The World Cup was won by which country?
16. Ulrike Maier, a World Champion, died in a race in which sport?
17. Liverpool appointed a new manager. Who was he?
18. Where were the Winter Olympics held?
19. Which Spaniard won the US Masters?
20. Which 51 year-old jockey won the Derby on Erhaab?
21. Who won the Scottish FA Cup?
22. Which England bowler took 9 wickets for 57 runs from just 99 balls in a Test against South Africa?
23. Who lost by four goals in the FA Cup final?
24. Which two female skaters hit the headlines after one attempted to get the other one "taken care of"?
25. Which Columbian defender was shot dead after he had scored an own goal in the World Cup?

A CENTURY OF SPORT – 1995. IN THIS YEAR...

1. The 1,000 Guineas was run on which day of the week for the first time?
2. Chris Eubank lost to which Irishman?
3. Who was voted the Football Writers' Player of the Year?
4. Who won the Premiership?
5. Which player, renowned for liking a drink, won the British Open at St Andrews?
6. Who won the League Cup?
7. Dominic Cork took a hat-trick in the Old Trafford Test against which team?
8. Who became the first team to score nine goals in a Premiership match?
9. Which famous horse, born on 3rd May 1965, died on 18th October?
10. Which Everton footballer was jailed for an assault perpetrated while a Rangers player?
11. Who won the Rugby World Cup?
12. Who became Leicester City manager in December 1995?
13. Which driver signed for McLaren but couldn't fit in the car?
14. Who did Blackburn Rovers lose to on the final day of the season, yet still won the Premiership?
15. What was the score in the Ashes series?
16. Who won the Australian Tennis Open at his first attempt?
17. Bruce Grobbelaar, John Fashanu and Hans Segers were all in the news over what allegations?
18. Eric Cantona kicked a fan during a match at which ground?
19. Who was the World Snooker Champion?
20. Arsenal lost in the Cup Winners' Cup to which team?
21. Which Chelsea player had an incident with a taxi driver?
22. Who were Ireland's opponents in a football friendly, which wasn't completed due to crowd trouble?
23. Peter Francisco was banned from which sport?
24. Who won the FA Cup?
25. Who scored the winning points in the Rugby World Cup final?

Answers to A CENTURY OF SPORT – 1993 IN THIS YEAR...
1. Monica Seles 2. True 3. Tony Tucker 4. Alex Ferguson 5. Nottingham Forest 6. Riddick Bowe 7. USA 8. Toronto Blue Jays 9. Ronnie O'Sullivan 10. Andy Linighan 11. Michael Atherton 12. Frank Bruno and Lennox Lewis 13. Cardiff 14. Captain Keith Brown 15. False. Man Utd 16. Graeme Hick 17. New Zealand 18. Sheffield Wednesday 19. The Belfry 20. Arthur Ashe 21. Stuttgart 22. Dallas Cowboys 23. France 24. Booby Moore 25. Greg Norman

A CENTURY OF SPORT – 1996. IN THIS YEAR...

1. Who stood down as England football coach this year?
2. Which British female athlete was banned from athletics for allegedly taking drugs only to be cleared of all charges?
3. What was the name of the mascot of the Atlanta Olympics Games?
4. Who scored the golden goal that won European Championships for Germany?
5. Alison Williamson went to the Atlanta games and represented Great Britain at the age of 14 in which sport?
6. Which Dutch player went home after he had a row with his coach during the European Nations Cup Finals?
7. Who scored the FA Cup winner?
8. What was the name of the mascot of Euro '96?
9. Who won the sixth Cricket World Cup?
10. Peter Shilton made his 1,000th league appearance in 1996 for which club?
11. Which Liverpool manager, born in 1919, died in 1996?
12. Who scored the only triple century in county cricket?
13. Which controversial decision gave Bath a victory by one point over Leicester in the Pilkington Cup final?
14. Which two clubs played rugby at Maine Road in the cross-code challenge?
15. Which legendary pool player died aged 62?
16. Who did Nick Faldo beat by five strokes to win the US Masters?
17. Who turned professional after winning the US Amateur Championship for the third time ?
18. What were the odds on Frankie Dettori's incredible seven out of seven winning streak at Ascot?
19. Which biking legend won his 21st Isle of Man TT race at the age of 44?
20. Which former tennis legend failed to make the cut at the Czech Golf Open?
21. What time did Michael Johnson record to shatter the existing 200m World Record in the Olympic final?
22. Who scored a century in the Cricket World Cup final?
23. Who bowled the West Indies out for a paltry 93 runs during the same tournament?
24. Tim Henman became the first British representative in the Men's Singles quarter-final since 1973. Who was the Briton on that occasion?
25. Who scored the winning goal in the FA Cup final?

Answers to A CENTURY OF SPORT – 1994. IN THIS YEAR...

1. Michael Schumacher *2.* Bobby Charlton *3.* Lennox Lewis *4.* Du'aine Ladejo *5.* America *6.* Diego Maradona *7.* Man Utd *8.* England *9.* No one (it was cancelled due to a players strike) *10.* John Toshack *11.* San Marinio Grand Prix *12.* Roland Ratenzenberger *13.* Dirt *14.* 45 *15.* Brazil *16.* Skiing *17.* Roy Evans *18.* Lillehammer *19.* Jose-Maria Olazabal *20.* Willie Carson *21.* Dundee Utd *22.* Devon Malcolm *23.* Chelsea *24.* Tonya Harding and Nancy Kerrigan *25.* Andres Escobar

A CENTURY OF SPORT – 1997. IN THIS YEAR...

1. How many golds did Britain win at the World Athletics Championships?
2. The World Athletics Championships took place in which city?
3. At Jerez, Schumacher was deemed to have made a big mistake by colliding with which driver?
4. Les Wallace became a World Champion in which sport?
5. Which team won the baseball World Series?
6. Which Heavyweight World Champion reported his sister to the police after she attacked him?
7. When Glamorgan won the County Championship, who was their overseas player?
8. The first goal of the FA Cup final was scored by which player?
9. Which record did that goal break?
10. The British Lions toured which country?
11. Who scored the fastest century of the county cricket season for the second year running and retained the Lawrence Trophy?
12. Which former England cricket captain was elevated to the House of Lords?
13. Which two cricketers were fined for an altercation during a Natwest semi-final?
14. Which two teams contested the tryless Pilkington Cup final?
15. What was unusual about the Grand National?
16. Which former FA Cup and League winner with Arsenal died aged 78?
17. Which England batsman scored a double hundred at Edgbaston?
18. Who scored two decisive centuries at Old Trafford to swing the Ashes series in Australia's favour?
19. Who scored Italy's winning goal at Wembley when they played England?
20. Who did Italy defeat in the play-off to qualify for the 1998 World Cup?
21. Who knocked Manchester United out of the Champions League and went on to upset Juventus in the final in Munich?
22. Who captained Europe to success in the Ryder Cup?
23. Who scored the vital drop-goal to secure the British Lions' Test series victory against South Africa?
24. Which snooker player ended Stephen Hendry's five-year unbeaten run at the Crucible?
25. Which Swiss miss became the youngest ever Grand Slam winner?

A CENTURY OF SPORT – 1998. IN THIS YEAR...

1. Michael Atherton resigned as England captain after how many Tests in charge?
2. What did the advertising campaign 'Stay at Home' attempt to prevent?
3. Which two McLaren drivers caused a bit of a stink following a private bet that whoever took the first corner could win the Australia Grand Prix?
4. Mark Ramprakash scored his maiden Test century against which team?
5. Who won the Grand National?
6. Who won the rugby league Challenge Cup?
7. Which Chelsea player named his child Beatrice Chelsea?
8. Roger Black ran his last race in which British stadium?
9. Which horse won the Derby?
10. England secured a memorable draw in the third cricket Test against South Africa at which ground?
11. Which country defeated the England rugby union team by a record 76-0 score?
12. By winning the Test Series against South Africa, England won their first five-match series since beating whom in 1986-87?
13. Following on from that, who was the captain on that occasion?
14. The Tour de France started from which city?
15. Who won the British Grand Prix?
16. How did Emma Brammer and Andrea Prime hit the news?
17. Who won the Tour de France?
18. Which (then) Newcastle Utd defender had a car crash just before the start of the season?
19. The European Athletics Championships took place in which city?
20. Who revealed in his book that he was unhappy that Alan Shearer was chosen ahead of him as England captain for France '98?
21. Which boat won the Whitbread Round the World yacht race?
22. Which European country hosted the World Shooting Championship?
23. Who was the Warwickshire cricket captain?
24. Which Irish swimmer was banned for tampering with her drug sample?
25. Which two teams contested the NBA final?

A CENTURY OF SPORT – 1999. IN THIS YEAR...

1. Robbie Keane became British football's most expensive teenager by moving from which club to Coventry City?
2. Who won cricket's County Championship?
3. The England rugby union team beat which country 106-8 at Twickenham?
4. How many gold medals did America win at the World Athletics Championships: 11, 12 or 13?
5. Which England rugby union international was fined £15,000 for bringing the game into disrepute?
6. Tony Banks was replaced by which woman as Sports Minister?
7. Who scored Scotland's Wembley winner during the Euro 2000 play-offs?
8. Who captained the European Ryder Cup team?
9. Australia defeated which team in the seventh Cricket World Cup final?
10. Wigan played which Super League team in the last match at Central Park?
11. Jason Jones-Hughes finally received clearance to play rugby union for Wales. In which country was he born?
12. Michael Johnson broke the World record for the 400m at the World Athletics Championships. What was his time?
13. America won the Ryder Cup at which course?
14. 'Shoot' magazine celebrated an anniversary. In which year was it first published?
15. Who published his autobiography, entitled 'Managing My Life'?
16. John Smith became the oldest person to swim the English Channel. How old was he: 65, 66 or 67?
17. Which young England bowler scored 99 not out in only his second Test?
18. Who was voted PFA Player of the Year?
19. Who did Wales play in the opening match of the Rugby World Cup?
20. Who won Ice Hockey's Stanley Cup?
21. How many centurions did England have during their Test series against New Zealand?
22. Who won the US Masters?
23. Which team won the NBA Championship?
24. Who broke the world record for the most points scored in international rugby union?
25. Which manager was acquitted of driving on the hard shoulder in order to beat a traffic jam, because he said he had "an upset stomach"?

Answers to A CENTURY OF SPORT – 1997. IN THIS YEAR...
1. None *2.* Athens *3.* Jacques Villeneuve *4.* Darts *5.* Florida Marlins *6.* Riddick Bowe *7.* Waqar Younis *8.* Roberto Di Matteo *9.* Quickest FA Cup Final Goal *10.* South Africa *11.* Graham Lloyd (73 balls v Leicestershire) *12.* Sir Colin Cowdrey *13.* Mark Ilott (Essex) and Robert Croft (Glamorgan) *14.* Leicester and Sale *15.* It was run on a Monday after a bomb-scare on the Saturday *16.* Denis Compton *17.* Nasser Hussain *18.* Steve Waugh *19.* Gianfranco Zola *20.* Russia *21.* Borussia Dortmund *22.* Seve Ballesteros *23.* Jeremy Guscott *24.* Ken Doherty *25.* Martina Hingis

CONNECTIONS -
WHAT CONNECTS ...

1. Dai Rees in 1957, Henry Cooper in 1967, Princess Anne in 1971 and Linford Christie in 1993?
2. 1959 Luton Town, 1964 Preston North End, 1978 Arsenal and 1983 Brighton & Hove Albion?
3. Wall Street, Diffident, Mark Of Esteem, Decorated Hero, Fatefully, Lochangel and Fujiyama Quest?
4. Wembley Stadium, London, Rotterdam and Camp Nou, Barcelona?
5. Ipswich, England, Sporting Libson, Porto, Barcelona, PSV Eindhoven and Newcastle Utd?
6. 'Make Up Maximum', 'Make Up Ticks' and 'Your Choice'?
7. Ray Reardon, Geoff Capes and Christopher Dean?
8. Uruguay 1930, Italy 1934 and France 1938?
9. Paul Gascoigne, Dion Dublin, Nicky Butt and Andy Hinchcliffe?
10. Brad Friedel, Alexei Lalas and Eric Wynalda?
11. What are Bleak, Rudd and Dace?
12. 'Upper Cut', 'A Man called Bulldozer' and 'Diamonds are as Red as Blood'
13. Apart from politics, what is the link between John Major, David Mellor and Tony Banks?
14. 1980 Indian Joe, 1990 Slippy Blue and 1994 Moral Standards?
15. Johnny Weismuller, Herman Brix, Glenn Morris and Buster Crabbe – aside from being Olympic Champions, what other connection do they have?
16. What are Okuri Dashi, Hataki Komi and Soto-Gake?
17. 1985 Rainbow Quest, 1986 Dancing Brave and 1987 Trampolino?
18. Warwickshire Cup, Queens Cup and the Huntwood Charity Day?
19. Stewie, Squeaky and Peter Perfect are all nicknames for whom?
20. 1977 The Minstrel, 1982 Golden Fleece and 1993 Commander-in-Chief?
21. Finn, Laser, Mistral and 470?
22. Leicester City 1978-85, Everton 1985-86, Barcelona 1986-89 and Spurs 1989-92?
23. Gordon Banks, Gary Lineker and Emile Heskey?
24. Trap 125, Skeet 125 and Double Trap 150 are all categories in which sport?
25. Green Room, Crystal Cathedral and Walking the Dog?

YOUNG SPORT

1. Fu Mingxia became world champ of which sport at the age of 12?
2. How old was Martina Hingis when she first won the Australian Open?
3. In 1972, who became the youngest ever player to win the World Snooker Championship?
4. Andrea Jaegar burnt herself out in which sport?
5. At what age did Lester Piggott ride his first Derby winner?
6. In 1980, which West Ham player became the youngest to play in an FA Cup final?
7. In 1949, who played cricket for England aged 18 years 149 days?
8. What does ESCA stands for?
9. In 1998, which 17-year-old amateur was the sensation of the British Open?
10. Who won the US Tennis Open in 1979 aged 16?
11. Mushtaq Mohammed played for which Test side aged 15 Years 124 days?
12. In 1988, who became the youngest person to score a hat-trick in the First Division aged 17 Years 240 days?
13. Who was the youngest ever winner of the British Golf Open?
14. In 1988, who became England's youngest ever rugby union captain?
15. How old was Don Bradman when he was selected for his first Test: 19, 20 or 21?
16. In 1950, who played football for Wales aged 18 years 71 days?
17. Who did Mike Tyson beat when he first became World Heavyweight Champion?
18. Who at the age of 18 scored in the FA Cup final for Man Utd in 1983?
19. Which Welsh international once captained England schoolboys?
20. Who was the youngest member of England's World Cup winning squad?
21. How old was Tiger Woods when he first won the US Amateur championship?
22. Anneka Reeder was a British Champion in which sport?
23. What is the youngest age at which a horse is permitted to ride in the Grand National?
24. In 1980, who won the US Masters aged 23?
25. At the age of 22, who became World chess champion in 1985?

MIXED BAG 16

1. Which football team's home ground is Maine Road?
2. How many points is the yellow worth in a game of snooker?
3. Cricketers sometimes wear what seems like war paint on their face. What is it?
4. On the France '98 Monopoly board which country was Park Lane?
5. Man Utd bought Dwight Yorke from which team?
6. Glenn Hoddle is a Hindu. True or false?
7. How many World Title fights did Frank Bruno have?
8. In Super League where do the Broncos come from?
9. The Sixfields Stadium is the new home of which football club?
10. What is the fewest number of points you need to win a game of tennis?
11. Henry and Robbie Paul are brothers who play which sport?
12. England play their home rugby union matches at which venue?
13. Who equalled Don Bradman's national record highest Test score against Pakistan in 1998?
14. Where did the Centennial Olympic Games take place?
15. Name the football club who play their home matches at the McAlpine Stadium.
16. Netball was invented in which country?
17. Which wrestler got his name from a Tennessee Williams character?
18. Which Richie was the first Australian cricketer to take 200 Test wickets and score 2000 Test runs?
19. Neville Southall played in goal for which country?
20. How many home runs did Mark McGuire hit in 1998 to surpass Roger Maris's 37-year old record of 61 in a season?
21. In American basketball who is the 'mailman'?
22. Which British boxer is a national hero in Yemen?
23. What is the WRU?
24. Which famous horse race takes place at Churchill Downs?
25. Name the English football team known as the 'Lions'?

BOXING HEAVIES 1

1. Who was the first American to win the Olympic heavyweight title?
2. In which city did Mike Tyson lose his World title against James Buster Douglas?
3. Which man remained World Heavyweight Champion for 11 years, 8 months and 12 days?
4. What nationality was the boxer Ingemar Johansson?
5. Lennox Lewis became WBC Champion after who threw his belt in the bin?
6. Who was the first black heavyweight World Champion?
7. 'Smokin Joe' was whose nickname?
8. Oliver McCall lost his World title against whom when he was disqualified for not defending himself?
9. David Tua is a boxer from which country?
10. How many times did Frank Bruno fight Mike Tyson?
11. When Cassius Clay first became World Champion, who did he beat in six rounds to win the title?
12. Who won the Olympic heavyweight gold in 1972, 1976 and 1980?
13. Which organisation did not officially recognise Lennox Lewis as their World Champion despite his defeat of Evander 'the Real Deal' Holyfield in November 1999?
14. Which boxing figure was born Monek Prager in Poland in 1929?
15. In the 1984 Olympics who won the super heavyweight gold?
16. How many World title fights did Rocky Marciano lose in his career?
17. Who was Frank Bruno's first World title fight against?
18. Which controversial referee, famous for giving Bugner his 1971 victory over Henry Cooper, died in November 1999 aged 79?
19. Ali fought whom in the 'Thriller in Manila'?
20. In the film Rocky III who played Clubber Lang?
21. Henry Cooper fought Ali how many times: once, twice or three times?
22. Which heavyweight do you associate with Norwich?
23. Who was called 'Madcap Maxie'?
24. In 1937 who fought Joe Louis under the proviso that he would get 10% of the profits of any future title for the next decade?
25. The female judge who scored Holyfield the winner against Lennox Lewis in their first fight came from where?

COUNTY CRICKET

1. Which county are known as the 'Sharks'?
2. Who holds the record for most wickets in a county season?
3. And in which year did Garfield Sobers hit them?
4. At the age of 16 Nigel Briers made his county debut for which club?
5. What is the highest ever first-class score?
6. David Bairstow kept wicket for which county?
7. Which cricket county has the daffodil as its emblem?
8. When Brian Lara scored his record 501 for Warwickshire, which county was he playing against?
9. What is 'Nelson' and why?
10. What is the name of the younger of the two Hollioake brothers?
11. 'Big Bird' played for Somerset. Who was he?
12. Devon Malcolm used to play for Derbyshire but now plays for which county?
13. In the summer of 1998 who became captain of Hampshire?
14. Which Yorkshire and England bowler has a black belt in karate and is a teetotaller?
15. How many County Championships have Durham won?
16. Which cricketer is known as 'Daffy'?
17. Which former Hampshire captain has the middle name Jefford?
18. Geoff Boycott holds the record for hitting the fastest ever County Championship Century. True or false?
19. Which is the oldest English cricket county club?
20. Who plays at Grace Road?
21. What is David Lawrence's nickname?
22. Ray Illingworth left which county to join Leicestershire in 1969?
23. Which twins made their first-class debut in 1939?
24. Graham Hick is a name associated with which county?
25. Who plays at Nevil Road?

SCOTTISH FOOTBALL

1. Rangers bought Gazza from which club?
2. Alex Ferguson's first managerial post was at which club?
3. Which striker played at Leeds Utd, Man Utd, AC Milan and Verona?
4. Rangers won which European trophy in 1972 by beating Dynamo Moscow 3-2?
5. During qualification for France '98 Scotland went to which country where the home side didn't turn up for the match?
6. Who plays at Easter Road?
7. Celtic won the European Cup in 1967. Who did they beat in the final?
8. When Scotland went to the World Cup in 1978 who was their manager?
9. Who won the Scottish Cup final in 1998?
10. 'We Have a Dream' was Scotland's song for which World Cup?
11. Rangers signed Duncan Ferguson from which club?
12. At the end of the 1997-98 Season who was bottom of the Scottish Premiership?
13. Graham Souness resigned as manager of which club to become Liverpool manager?
14. What was Scotland's official World Cup song for France '98?
15. How many times has Scotland made it to the second round of the World Cup finals?
16. By going to France '98, which Scotland player made his fourth appearance in the World Cup Finals?
17. The Scottish Football Association was formed in which year?
18. Andrei Kanchelskis left which club to join Rangers?
19. Who was the first man to play 100 times for Scotland?
20. In 1990 which two teams played in the first game to be broadcast by BSkyB in Britain?
21. Who scored a spectacular individual goal against Holland in the 1978 World Cup?
22. Who won the first Scottish FA Cup?
23. Partick Thistle play at which ground?
24. What position did Scotland finish in their group at France '98.
25. Which Scottish team are known as the 'Blue Brazil'?

CRYING

1. Which Czech tennis player cried after losing to Steffi Graf in the 1993 Wimbledon Final?
2. Why did Mary Decker blub at the LA Olympics?
3. Which golfer had a putt to retain the Ryder cup in 1991 for Europe but missed it?
4. Ato Boldon was devastated after only finishing third in the 100m final at the Atlanta Olympics but on whom did he blame his defeat?
5. Which Bayern Munich player was reduced to tears following Manchester United's two injury-time goals in the 1999 European Champions League final?
6. Kim Hughes was shown crying on Australian TV in 1984 as he resigned the Australian cricket captaincy. Which team beat them in the Brisbane Test?
7. Which snooker player opened the floodgates after winning the 1982 World Championship?
8. Which little cox cried his heart out for Britain when he won proudly won a gold at the Olympics?
9. Which man cried when he won the 1982 World Darts Championship?
10. Which Brazilian coach cried after beating Holland to reach the final of France '98?
11. In 1966 who shed a big tear after winning his first British Open at Muirfield?
12. When England won the World Cup which No 5 broke down and cried with joy?
13. Anton Geesink made the Japanese cry when he won an Olympic gold beating their man in the final of which sport?
14. Why did Richard Virenque break down and cry at the 1998 Tour de France?
15. Gary Lineker made Gazza cry in which advert?
16. Roger Black was not happy when he finished second in the 400m final at the 1994 European championships. Which Briton beat him?
17. Which heavyweight champion cried after beating Joe Louis in 1951?
18. Who cried after losing his title to Lennox Lewis in the rematch?
19. Which British female middle distance runner was one of the favourites to win a medal at the 1997 World Championships until she got injured?
20. In 1966 the Portuguese striker Eusebio was distraught after losing in the World Cup semi-final to which team?
21. Mike Powell couldn't stop which man winning the long jump at the Atlanta Games to his great dismay?
22. Which 19-year-old Spaniard cried for Europe in the 1999 Ryder Cup?
23. In which year did Nick Faldo go all tearful when he won the British Open for the third time?
24. Which female tearful athlete was BBC Sports Personality of the Year in 1987?
25. Which team tragically lost two World Cup finals in the 1970's?

MIXED BAG 17

1. How many points is the green worth in a game of snooker?
2. Kickboxing and Thai-boxing are the same. True or false?
3. The first modern Olympics took place in 1896 in which city?
4. Which famous funnyman and impressionist of the 1970's and early 80's had trials for Oldham Athletic and Stockport County?
5. What does RFU stand for?
6. Which chess player is known as the 'Beast of Baku'?
7. Who rode his first Derby winner on a horse called Never Say Die?
8. 'The Battling Guardsman' was another name of which wrestler?
9. Which baseball player was known as the 'Sultan of Swat'?
10. In the early 80's which tennis player said he only played at Wimbledon because his clothing and racquet contracts stipulated so?
11. In the last England v. Scotland game of the century, Scotland triumphed 1-0. But who won the first game of the century?
12. Which county cricket team are known as the 'Lions'?
13. 'Bert Trautmann's Helmet' is a fanzine from which football club?
14. Which tycoon failed to buy Man Utd in 1998?
15. Why is the Derby so called?
16. Pot Black is a trophy linked with which sport?
17. Which legendary baseball player was asked what he thought of being paid more money in a year than President Hoover and replied: "I had a better year than he did"?
18. Who wrote the stage play 'An evening with Gary Lineker'?
19. The Madejski Stadium is the home of which football club?
20. In basketball how many points do you get for a 'slam dunk'?
21. Which game does Nigel Short play?
22. The Poole Pirates play which sport?
23. Which baseball player was known as the 'Yankee Clipper'?
24. Who was World Heavyweight Champion from 1919 to 1926?
25. How was the term 'back to square one' invented?

CYCLING

1. What colour jersey does the leader of the Tour de France wear?
2. Which cyclist built an unusual but highly effective bike out of washing machine spares?
3. What is the Peleton?
4. What nationality is Eddie Merckx?
5. Which man won the Tour de France and prevented Miguel Indurain from winning an unprecedented sixth successive title?
6. Who is known as 'Big Mig'?
7. Who was called 'the Cannibal'?
8. Which British cyclist died during the Tour de France in 1967?
9. Which two mountain ranges does the Tour traditionally take in?
10. What does the term 'Lantern Rouge' mean?
11. Kevin Costner and David Grant play two brothers in which cycling film?
12. Mountain Biking made its Olympic debut at which games?
13. When was the first Tour of Britain held?
14. Who is known as 'the Pirate' or 'the flying elephant'?
15. Who became the first German to win the Tour de France in 1997?
16. What does BMX stand for?
17. Who became the first Irishman to win the Tour de France in 1987?
18. Which cyclist won BBC Sports Personality of the Year in 1965?
19. Banesto, ONCE, Kelme and Vitali Clio are all teams from which country?
20. Which all-time great was called the 'badger'?
21. The Cycling World Cup took place for the first time in 1989 in which riders amassed points over 12 races. Which Irishman won the inaugural title?
22. The first Tour de France was held in which year: 1903, 1913 or 1923?
23. The UCI governs cycling now. What does it stand for?
24. Which Frenchman lost the 3,500-mile Tour de France to Greg LeMond by just eight seconds in 1989 and has never discussed this narrow defeat since?
25. What is Contre Le Montre more commonly known as?

DARTS

1. In a game of darts how many points is the Bull worth?
2. What is the maximum checkout?
3. What does BDO stand for?
4. Which larger than life darts player described as having all the glitter of Gary with a touch of Ron Atkinson?
5. Brian Gamlin died in 1903. What did he do with regard to darts?
6. "I need six or seven pints and half a dozen trips to the gents before I'm ready to play" was a quote by which former Welsh dartist?
7. Which two players recorded the song '180'?
8. Which Scot met his wife when he delivered coal to her front door covered head to foot in dust?
9. How many points is the Outer Bull worth?
10. Which numbers are either side of the 20?
11. Who was the Dutchman who became Embassy World Champion in 1998?
12. How many times was Eric Bristow World Darts Champion in the 80's?
13. In a game of darts what double are you on if you are 'in the basement'?
14. Which darts player lost his false teeth as he gave a yell to celebrate a victory, when they dropped out and smashed on the floor?
15. Who has the nickname 'the Bronze Adonis'?
16. In which year was the first World Darts Championship held?
17. Who won it?
18. In the first World Championship which Englishman lost in the final?
19. The Pilgrim Fathers played darts on the Mayflower when on their voyage to the New World. True or false?
20. What is Eric Bristow's nickname?
21. The NDA was formed in 1924. What does it stand for?
22. Who was the first Scotsman to win the World Darts Championship?
23. In which year did the BBC first televise darts?
24. What is the line called that you throw your darts from?
25. At what type of vessels did First World War pilots aim darts?

FLAT RACING

1. In which year was Shergar kidnapped?
2. The Kentucky Derby is always in which month?
3. Which place is Glorious?
4. Frankie Dettori won all the races on the card at which course in 1996?
5. Every year at Royal Ascot, the jockey with the most winners receives which award?
6. How many times did Lester Piggott win the Derby?
7. Who was the suffragette who threw herself under the King's horse in the Derby in 1913?
8. Which jockey was knighted in June 1953?
9. Which course traditionally hosts the St.Leger?
10. In America what is the Triple Crown?
11. Which BBC pundit and former Question of Sport captain was also five times champion jockey?
12. The Millionaires' race is the tag given to which horse race?
13. Aliysa finished first in 1989 but was then disqualified in which race?
14. Steve Cauthen is a jockey from which country?
15. Mohammed Al-Maktoum removed all his horses from which trainer in 1995?
16. Who won more races – Lester Piggott or Sir Gordon Richards?
17. The Derby is run over what distance?
18. The Coronation Stakes takes place at which course?
19. If a jockey is a 'pork butcher' what does it mean?
20. Who was the owner of Shergar?
21. 'Pat on the Back' is a book about whom?
22. Lord Glasgow used to do what to his horses in the 19th century if they didn't come up to scratch?
23. Name the five Classics.
24. The Kentucky Derby is run at which racecourse?
25. In 1988, Diminuendo and Melodist were in a dead heat in which race?

MIXED BAG 18

1. Tottenham play their homes games at which ground?
2. Who lost in the World Snooker Championship final of 1998?
3. Vladi Dwak is a basketball player from which country?
4. John Fashanu's brother died in 1998. What was his name?
5. Who was the first female to captain a cricket team at Lord's?
6. The Summer Olympics took place at which city in 1988?
7. In which city were the first Summer Olympics held after the Second World War?
8. Which running legend was the chairman of the Sports Council from 1971-74?
9. Who are Saint and Greavsie?
10. The Seaslug was a champion in which sport?
11. Who were the first British football team to play in Europe?
12. In nautical terms what is right?
13. 'Empty Hand' is the English translation of the name of which martial art?
14. The Bunbury could have been the name of which famous horserace if Sir Charles Bunbury had won the toss of a coin?
15. Which World Cup winner advertised the Irish Fishing board in the 90's?
16. The Pohang Steelers are a football team from which country?
17. 'Through The Wind and Rain' is a fanzine from which football club?
18. 'Whispering Death' was the nickname of which famous fast bowler?
19. The Arthur Ashe Stadium is in which sport?
20. Who is Venus Williams's younger sister?
21. What is ex-FIFA President Joao Havelenge's nationality?
22. In 1994 which country won the women's Rugby World Cup?
23. Which golfer unfortunately died in 1999 aboard his private jet?
24. Fred Trueman played his cricket for which county?
25. "Look, I tried to tell you how great I was but you chumps wouldn't listen." Muhammed Ali said this to reporters after beating whom?

JARGON

1. In betting terms what odds is a 'carpet'?
2. 'Cross-overs' and the 'kempa trick' are terms from which sport?
3. In South Africa what is a 'brain bucket'?
4. 'Cannon peg out' and 'triple peel' are all terms from which sport?
5. In which sport could you perform 'a sacrfice fly'?
6. What are 'Scooby Doos' in ten-pin bowling?
7. In a game of hurling what is the Sliothar ?
8. What is an 'Alley Oop'?
9. Which score do Australians consider unlucky in cricket?
10. What is 'choking' in sporting terms?
11. What is an Ippon?
12. In baseball what is the play called when the batter deliberately hits the ball softly so he can get on base or a team mate can move on to another base?
13. If you 'nail' a somersault what does it mean?
14. Who is a surfer talking about when they mention a 'goat boater'?
15. What's the stick in golf?
16. If a yachtsman or woman 'turns turtle' what does it mean?
17. In English cricket it's a googly. What is it called in Australia?
18. If you win by a sweep in American sport what have you done?
19. In baseball what is an RBI?
20. What is a TKO in boxing?
21. In golf what is a Mulligan?
22. In tennis it's not called 40 all but what?
23. A Gromit is what in surfing?
24. What is a manhole-cover in hockey?
25. What is 'cabbage' in golf?

MARTIAL ARTS

1. Taekwondo originates from which country?
2. What is called the 'Gentle Game'?
3. Bruce Lee died in which year?
4. Brian Jacks is a name associated with which martial art?
5. Aikido comes from Japan. True or false?
6. Which Man Utd player performed a Kung Fu kick on a Crystal Palace fan?
7. Shotokan is a style from which martial art?
8. Which martial art uses bamboo sticks?
9. At which Olympics was judo introduced?
10. "Wax on, Wax off" was a phrase used in which film?
11. The World Karate Championship first took place in 1970. Which country won the men's team competition?
12. Mitsuru Kobayashi was the first world champion of which discipline?
13. Bruce Lee devised which TV show?
14. Judo is derived from which other martial art?
15. Professor Jigoro Kano is credited with inventing which martial art?
16. What is a sensei?
17. Which martial art is generally acknowledged as having been brought from Okinawa to Japan by a man called Funakoshi Gichin?
18. Kung Fu originated in which country?
19. "The way of the sword" is a translation of which martial art?
20. How is Shinobi more commonly known?
21. What is a Dojo?
22. Which man was the star in the TV show Kung Fu?
23. Kung Fu has origins in which religion?
24. Ju-Jitsu comes from which country?
25. Kenpo is derived from which other martial art?

DEFENDERS

1. Which football pundit played 26 times for Scotland, and also represented this country at golf and volleyball?
2. Which man played 77 times for England, joined Rangers in 1986 and later became an inspirational captain?
3. In 1998, which defender left West Ham to join Aston Villa but within two days had decided that he had made a mistake and signed for Everton instead?
4. Which Crystal Palace and Arsenal left back made 86 England appearances between 1979 and 1988?
5. What is Stuart Pearce's nickname?
6. Which Liverpool full-back was bought from Northampton Town in 1974 and missed only one league game in 10 seasons?
7. Man Utd bought Jaap Stam from which Dutch club?
8. Which West Ham hardman's book was called 'Terminator – The Authorised story'?
9. Between 1975 and 1993, David O'Leary played for which club?
10. In 1998, Colin Hendry left Blackburn to join which club?
11. What nationality is Slaven Bilic?
12. Which England World Cup winner later became an undertaker?
13. Tommy Smith played for Everton. True or false?
14. Which defender captained the 1978 World Cup winners?
15. Who was the first player to be sent off in an FA Cup final?
16. Viv Anderson first played for England in which year?
17. Which Scottish defender scored against Brazil in the 1982 World Cup Finals?
18. What was the title of Tony Adams' autobiography, in which he was critical of Hoddle's tactics in the 1998 World Cup?
19. Which of the Neville Brothers didn't make it to France in 1998?
20. Jimmy Armfield only played for one club. Which club?
21. Who was England's no 5 when they won the 1966 World Cup?
22. Who captained West Germany to victory in the 1974 World Cup?
23. Which Nottingham Forest and England defender unwittingly scored the winning goal for Spurs in the 1991 FA Cup final?
24. Which French defender missed the 1998 World Cup final following a red card in the semi-final?
25. Which Manchester United defender was denied a goal in the 1991 Cup Winner's Cup final because a team-mate touched the ball over the line?

MIXED BAG 19

1. Karren Brady is a name linked with which Midlands football club?
2. Which team does Craig Chalmers play International rugby for?
3. Who became Man City manager in 1972, resigned in 1973 and returned as manager in 1979?
4. Over how many miles is the 2,000 Guineas run?
5. In which year did Barcelona host the Summer Olympics?
6. In Australia what is the MCG?
7. CF is what position in baseball?
8. How many hurdles are there in a 110 metres hurdles: 8, 10, or 12?
9. Where do Rangers play their home games?
10. Which film depicted the true story of Harold Abrahams and Eric Liddell?
11. What is it called if you drop the ball in American Football when in possession?
12. In which American city would you find the Hubert Humphrey Metrodome?
13. John and Michael Whitaker are two brothers connected with which sport?
14. With which sport would associate Brett Favre?
15. Argentina's top scorer for the national side was whom before Batistuta?
16. Which snooker player was also known as 'PC 184'?
17. The Prix de L'Arc de Triomphe takes place in which month?
18. Which Australian revolutionised cricket in the 1970's by creating World Series Cricket?
19. 'The Bad News Bears' is a film based around which sport?
20. Which American Football team moved from Baltimore to Indianapolis in 1983?
21. Bull riding, calf roping and team roping are 3 events in which sport?
22. Old Trafford is the ground of which cricket county?
23. Which basketball player retired from the game to play baseball for the Birmingham Barons?
24. What does CIPS stand for?
25. Which famous British jockey rode 4,870 winners between 1920 and 1954?

RUGBY UNION

1. 'Coochie' is the nickname of which ex-England prop?
2. How many people make up a rugby union team?
3. In English rugby who are the 'Tigers'?
4. What did the JPR stand for in JPR Williams?
5. What was Sean Fitzpatrick's position?
6. South Africa are called the Springboks, New Zealand the All-Blacks but what are Argentina called?
7. Gavin Hastings played for which side in the Varsity match?
8. The Middlesex Sevens takes place at which ground?
9. Gordon who played in the second row on three British Lions Tours?
10. Whilst on tour with the Lions in 1971 who was called the 'King'?
11. Who are the 'Friendly Islands'?
12. In which New Zealand city is Eden Park?
13. Which Fijian is generally regarded as the best ever sevens player?
14. When the Lions toured South Africa in 1997, who was their captain?
15. Which team won the first ever Heineken Trophy?
16. Which two Premiership clubs folded in the summer of 1999?
17. The Calcutta Cup was played on which day of the week in 1998?
18. In New Zealand who are the Blues?
19. Which is the world's oldest rugby club?
20. 'Living With The Lions' was a documentary about which tour?
21. The World Cup final took place at which ground in 1995?
22. Erica Roe's infamous streak took place in which year?
23. Which Tony was a flanker for Broughton Park and played 43 times for England?
24. Which country was the first northern hemisphere side to win a Test series in New Zealand?
25. When South Africa won the 1995 World Cup who was their only black player?

NEW ZEALAND SPORT

1. Sir Richard Hadlee played cricket for which county?
2. Jeff Wilson chose to play rugby union having played at international level in which other sport?
3. What is the war dance that the All-Blacks always perform before their matches called?
4. Who did Will Carling call a 'freak of nature'?
5. Which city hosted the Commonwealth Games in 1990?
6. Which Kiwi is said to have been the first man to reach the summit of Everest?
7. Which Kiwi died testing one of his cars at Goodwood in 1970?
8. Which New Zealander won the Olympic 800m title in 1960 and 1964?
9. Who won Olympic gold on a horse called Charisma?
10. Did New Zealand first play Test cricket before or after India?
11. Barry Briggs and Ivan Mauger are names from which sport?
12. Murt O'Donoghue is recognised as the first man to do what in 1934?
13. Who do New Zealand play in the Bledisloe Cup?
14. Ken Rosewall was a famous tennis star from New Zealand. True or false?
15. 22 African countries staged a boycott of the 1976 Olympics because New Zealand's rugby team had toured which country?
16. In 1906 and 1912 New Zealand hosted it instead of Australia. What was it?
17. Described by some as the most famous horse of all time, it was bought in New Zealand in 1927 at a yearling sale. What was its name?
18. Kiwi Cyril Browlee was the first man to be sent off in an international in which sport?
19. In which century was rugby introduced to New Zealand?
20. Who was the first Kiwi golfer to win the British Open?
21. Who did New Zealand play in an infamous one-day International, when the last ball was bowled underarm?
22. The Ranfurly Shield is played for in which sport?
23. After the 1995 Rugby World Cup, Jonah Lomu got offers to play which other sports?
24. 'A Hell of a Way To Earn A Living' is a book by which Kiwi?
25. Michael Campbell plays which sport?

MIXED BAG 20

1. What nationality is Ruud Gullit?
2. Which horse won the 2,000 Guineas in 1998?
3. Name the player who came back from a ban to be the top scorer at the 1982 World Cup?
4. The inaugural Gridiron World Bowl took place in which year of the 1990's?
5. Malcolm Allison used to wear what sort of hat until the FA banned it, claiming that it incited violence?
6. How many gold medals did Jesse Owens win at the Berlin Olympics?
7. When an athlete talks about 'smarties' what do they mean?
8. The 1932 Summer Olympics took place in which city?
9. Persepolis is a top football team from which country?
10. Henry Blofeld commentates on which sport?
11. Tony Kukoc is a name from which sport?
12. Nat Lofthouse is a name linked with which football club?
13. In which gymnastic discipline would a man do the 'scissors'?
14. Which well-known British racing driver has the middle names Ernest James?
15. Which sportsman got his name from a character from the book 'Cat on a Hot Tin Roof'?
16. What type of fish is a gonk?
17. Norris Williams survived the sinking of which boat to win Olympic and Wimbledon Titles?
18. Which man was chosen as the European Ryder Cup captain of 1999?
19. Which Czech man dominated the 1952 Olympics and ended up cleaning streets of Prague in the 1970's?
20. Which British decathlete got into trouble for whistling during the national anthem?
21. In 1998, which cricketer was appointed captain of Derbyshire?
22. Which three times World Grand Prix champion also represented his country at clay pigeon shooting?
23. The Houston Rockets play baseball. True or false?
24. Which ice hockey player retired in 1999 after dominating the sport throughout his career?
25. What is the Swedish method of training called, which is characterised by running hard and slow alternately?

GOLF 1

1. Who is known as the 'Great White Shark'?
2. The US Masters takes place at which course?
3. When Greg Norman went into the final round of the 1996 Masters, how many strokes did he lead by?
4. The Ryder Cup was held in which country in 1997?
5. If you score three under par on one hole, what is this called?
6. The 1998 British Open was held at which course?
7. What nationality was Bobby Locke?
8. In golf what is the 19th hole?
9. Which golfer was named after a friend of his father's who didn't come back from the Vietnam War?
10. How often is the Ryder Cup played?
11. A nervous disability that impairs your putting stroke is called what?
12. What's the male amateur equivalent of the Ryder Cup?
13. The first US Women's Open was in which decade: 1940's, 50's or 60's?
14. If Tiger Woods had won the 1998 Masters he would have become the third man to win two Masters titles on the trot. Name the first two men who have achieved this feat?
15. If the angle on your iron is flatter, does it mean the ball will go further or shorter?
16. In how many British Opens did Ben Hogan compete?
17. In which year did Great Britain and Ireland become Europe in the Ryder Cup?
18. What is a 'gimmie' in golf?
19. Wentworth is in which English county?
20. The Volvo PGA Championship took place at which course in 1998?
21. Who was the first man to win the British and US Open in the same year?
22. Who is the Golden Bear?
23. "If I'd been born within walking distance of a gym, I wouldn't mind betting I'd be Welterweight Champ of the World" was a quote from which portly golfer?
24. What is the WPGA?
25. The first recorded golf tournament for women took place in which year?

EUROPEAN TROPHIES

1. The European Cup was first contested in which decade of the 20th Century?
2. Which team won the last European Cup Winners' Cup in 1999?
3. Which Italian club side featured three Dutch greats in their European Cup winning teams of the late 80's?
4. Following on from that, who were the three players?
5. Who were the first Dutch team to lift the European Cup?
6. When Man Utd won the European Cup in 1968, who did they beat in the final?
7. Why were Celtic forced to replay a European Cup-tie with Rapid Vienna at Old Trafford in 1985?
8. It used to be called the Inter-Cities Fairs Cup. What is it now called?
9. When Man Utd were banned from playing any European Cup-ties within 100 miles of Old Trafford in the mid-70's, where did they play their home games?
10. When Celtic won the European Cup in the 60's who did they beat in the final?
11. Which Scottish team lost in the first European Cup Winners Cup final?
12. In 1963 which British team became the first to win a European football trophy by winning the Cup Winners' Cup?
13. Which European football trophy was first won by Fiorentina in 1961?
14. Which country won the European Football Championship in 1964?
15. Gareth Southgate missed a penalty in Euro '96 against which team?
16. When Chelsea won the Cup Winners Cup in 1998 who did they beat in the final?
17. Which paper had the headline of "Swedes 2 Turnips 1" after England lost in the European Championship?
18. Before the fall of the Iron Curtain, which was the only Eastern Bloc team to win the European Cup?
19. Bob Paisley's Liverpool team first won the European Cup in which year?
20. Which English football team won the European Cup in 1980?
21. British clubs won the European Cup six years running from 1977 to 1982. Which British club were the successful team in 1982?
22. Gabriel Hanot came up with the idea of which European football trophy?
23. Which ageing German midfield legend wanted to throw away his European Cup loser's medal in 1999?
24. The first country to win the European Football Championship was USSR in 1960. True or false?
25. Which team won the first five European Cups?

ITALIAN SPORT

1. Where does the Italian Grand Prix take place?
2. Italy lost the 1994 World Cup final to which team?
3. Who is Paulo Maldini's father?
4. Costantino Rocca is a name associated with which sport?
5. Which football team won the UEFA Cup in 1998?
6. Who was the Chelsea striker dropped by his country for France '98?
7. Edorado Mangiarotti won thirteen Olympic medals in which sport?
8. In which year did Rome host the Summer Olympics?
9. How many times has Italy hosted the World Cup Finals?
10. Mario Cipollini is a name associated with which sport?
11. Who did the Italian Stallion fight in 'Rocky'?
12. The Heysel Stadium disaster was in which year?
13. Chelsea signed Gianfranco Zola from which club?
14. Who was manager of the Italian football team at the 1994 World Cup?
15. The second World Athletics Championships took place in 1987 in which Italian city?
16. Which man won the 200m at the 1980 Olympics and was known as the 'Blue Arrow'?
17. AC and Inter Milan both play at which ground?
18. Name the famous Italian team who play in black and white striped shirts?
19. Frankie Dettori supports which London football team?
20. In which sport is the Giro D'Italia?
21. Which Welsh striker said of his move to Italy in 1988: "It's like going to a different country"?
22. Where is the San Marino Grand Prix held?
23. Oliver Bierhoff left Udinese to join which Italian giants?
24. Sampdoria are based in which Italian city?
25. Fiona May used to compete for Britain, but she changed her allegiance to Italy. Which is her event?

MIXED BAG 21

1. How much is the black ball worth in snooker?
2. Heath Streak is a fast bowler with which Test Side?
3. Which Yorkshire football club plays at home at Oakwell?
4. Zinedine Zidane is a footballer from which country?
5. Which team won the first World Bowl?
6. Which rugby country's home ground is Landsdowne Road?
7. Bryan Robson captained England for the first time in which year?
8. Peter Alliss commentates on which sport?
9. The summer Olympics of 1972 took place in which city?
10. In rugby union who is 'Deano'?
11. Spurs bought Darren Anderton from which football club?
12. In baseball, what position is 1B?
13. Which Grand Slam tennis tournament takes place at Flushing Meadow?
14. In 9-ball pool what colour is the number 1?
15. Steve Coppell was manager of which club for 30 days?
16. Which game takes its name from a school in Warwickshire?
17. Ervin Johnson is better known as which famous basketballer?
18. What is the 'going' in horse racing?
19. Chester-le-Street is the home of which county cricket team?
20. Which heavyweight defended his World crown for a total of 169 rounds?
21. Which tennis star, known as 'Jimbo', won Wimbledon twice, in 1974 and 1982?
22. Who lost both the 1998 and 1999 FA Cup finals?
23. In American Football, what is the move called when safties line up with the defensive line to go after the QB instead of the receivers and running backs?
24. Which European country held the first World Indoor Athletics Championship in 1985?
25. What is a 'flipper' in cricketing terms?

DRUGS

1. From which sport was Yuan-Yuan banned in 1998?
2. Which Canadian had his gold for snowboarding briefly removed after he tested positive for marijuana?
3. Which female British athlete was banned from competing and later won her appeal after she protested her innocence, claiming that her urine sample had been wrongly stored?
4. Paul Edwards became the first British athlete to be banned for life for using performance enhancing drugs. What was his sport?
5. Which famous England cricketer was banned in 1986 after admitting he had used cannabis?
6. In weightlifting, how many attempts are you allowed to lift a weight?
7. Which South African heavyweight was stripped of the IBF title for taking drugs?
8. Which Canadian snooker player was banned for using cocaine?
9. In 1995, South Africa's Liza de Villiers became the youngest athlete to fail a drug test after having anabolic steroids in her system. How old was she?
10. Which former England cricketer was refused entry into America in 1998 because of a drug conviction?
11. Which player missed out on breaking the World Cup Finals appearances record in 1994, after testing positive?
12. What is DHT?
13. Roger Stanislaus became the first footballer in this country to test positive for which drug?
14. 'Rock Bottom' is a book by which former coke addict?
15. In 1998, which cycling team's masseur was apprehended before the Tour de France when steroids and other banned substances were found in his car?
16. In drugs what is HGH?
17. Ed Giddins was banned from cricket for taking cocaine, prior to moving to Warwickshire. Which county did he play for at the time?
18. Katrina Krabbe was an athlete from which country?
19. In 1979 a horse called No Bombs was disqualified after winning a race at Worcester because caffeine was found in its system. What was it later proved to have eaten?
20. Which Frenchman won the French Tennis Open in 1983 and later said that he'd been smoking dope throughout the tournament?
21. Which well-known English 400m runner was convicted in the US of drug-dealing?
22. Dwight Gooden and Darryl Strawberry are two high-profile names from which sport who have had drug problems in the past?
23. Lawrence Taylor was a hulk of man who played which sport in America?
24. At which Olympics were dope tests for all medallists introduced?
25. Jennifer Capriati liked grass in more ways than one. What is her sport?

FOOTBALL MUSIC

1. 'Nice One Cyril' is a song associated with which football club?
2. In 1979, who released a single called 'Head Over Heels'?
3. Which player rapped on the track 'World in Motion'?
4. Who did Sunderland's song attempt to cheer up?
5. "30 years of hurt, Never stopped us dreaming" is a line from which song?
6. What was England's official World Cup song for France '98 called?
7. Who was the Ossie in 'Ossie's Dream'?
8. 'Do the Right Thing' was a song by which Arsenal striker?
9. Man Utd had a No 1 hit with 'Come on you Reds' in which year?
10. What was the Arsenal FA Cup song of 1998 called?
11. 'I'm Forever Blowing Bubbles' is a song associated with which club?
12. Fat Les had a hit record in 1998 with which song?
13. Which group performed Scotland's official France '98 song?
14. Which band wrote 'All I want for Christmas is a Dukla Prague Away Kit'?
15. 'The Whole World At Our Feet' was England's World Cup song in which year?
16. Which band helped inspire Manchester United to the Double in 1994?
17. 'Back Home' was a No 1 hit in 1970. True or false?
18. Andy Cameron sang which song for Scotland in 1978?
19. Leeds Utd reached No 10 in 1972 with which song?
20. The Gallagher brothers from Oasis support which football team?
21. During the 1980's, Chas & Dave sang with which football team?
22. 'The Anfield Rap' was supposed to inspire Liverpool to beat which football team in the 1988 FA Cup final?
23. 'Here We Go' was which club's first charting single?
24. In 1983 it was 'Glory Glory' for whom?
25. 'Easy Easy' was a World Cup song for Scotland in which year?

MIXED BAG 22

1. Zola Budd used to have a poster of Mary Decker above her bed. True or false?
2. Who was the captain of the 1970 World Cup winning team?
3. What is a GS in netball?
4. Name the famous manager, who as a player, played twice for England and scored 251 goals in 274 games as a centre forward?
5. The 1952 Summer Olympics were held in which city?
6. The Brazilian Grand Prix is held at which track?
7. In men's golf, which of the four Majors took place for the first time in 1916?
8. In 1989 the St.Leger was ran at which course?
9. Henry Cotton is a name linked with which sport?
10. In 1973 who trained for a fight with Ken Norton by cutting down trees?
11. Which two clubs contested the Worthington Cup final of 1999?
12. Where was the US Open Tennis held before it moved to Flushing Meadow?
13. 'It's Much More Important Than That' is a book about which football great?
14. In 1998 Ally McCoist left Rangers to join which team?
15. What is a 'Dan' in martial arts?
16. In American Football, when a quarterback deliberately throws the ball away to avoid being sacked what is this called?
17. Which England cricket captain was turned down for national service in South Africa because of his epilepsy?
18. Whose autobiography is called 'Mr Wright'?
19. Which goalkeeper and captain lifted the 1982 World Cup?
20. Who was the first unseeded man to win the singles title at Wimbledon?
21. What is Ellery Hanley's sport?
22. Which female hurdler advertised Quorn?
23. Loftus Road is the home of which football club?
24. The first Winter Olympics was held in which year?
25. Which 107 year-old Australian cricket competition changed its name to the Pura Milk Cup in 1999?

FRENCH SPORT

1. What takes place at Roland Garros?
2. Oliver Peslier is regarded as one of the world's best what?
3. Frenchman Henri Delauney created the European Football Championships. In which year were they first held?
4. Name the only French woman to win both the 200 and 400 metres at the same Olympics
5. What is France's national stadium called?
6. Yannick Noah is a name linked with which sport?
7. In which year did France first win the European Championships?
8. The Prix de l'Arc de Triomphe takes place at which French racecourse?
9. Which former French MP was the chairman of Marseille until his dodgy dealings were revealed?
10. What is the Maillot Jaune?
11. Which French footballer was voted the English Football Writers' Player of the Year in 1996?
12. Who are PSG?
13. What was the official mascot of France '98?
14. In 1999, which French Premiership player claimed that the English league was the dirtiest in the world?
15. Who knocked France out of the 1995 Rugby World Cup?
16. Baron Pierre de Coubertin was the founder of which global event?
17. France defeated which team in France '98 by a golden goal?
18. The French invented tennis. True or false?
19. How many times have France played in the World Cup final?
20. Which player was blamed for France's failure to qualify for the 1994 World Cup after he lost the ball in the last minute against Bulgaria, which in turn led to them scoring and knocking France out?
21. "1966 was a great year for British football." According to the advert, it was because which player was born that year?
22. In which year did France host its first Football World Cup?
23. Which French footballer was voted PFA Player of the Year in 1999?
24. Which famous competition do the French call the 'big loop'?
25. How many shots could Jean Van de Velde have taken on the last hole of the 1999 Open to win?

WORLD CUP '98

1. In terms of population, which was the smallest nation at France '98?
2. Who did Terry Venables' Australian team lose to in a World Cup play-off?
3. The first game of France '98 was between which two teams?
4. Which team won their final match 6-1 but were still knocked out of the tournament?
5. Which team, who didn't make it to France '98, had the misfortune of having their bare feet beaten by a cane as punishment?
6. The 'Super Eagles' appeared at France '98. Who are they?
7. How many teams qualified for the finals in France?
8. Which Scot was the oldest player at France '98?
9. Bo Johannson was the coach of which team?
10. Which Brazilian party-animal scored five goals in the 1994 finals but didn't make it to France '98 because of injury?
11. Who was the first player to receive a yellow card at France '98?
12. Who was the first man to be sent off at France '98?
13. How many goals did Gabrielle Batistuta score at France '98?
14. Which Colombian striker was sent home for undermining the squad's morale?
15. Which man scored the first goal of France '98?
16. The opening match of the tournament took place at which stadium?
17. Naughty Mokoena was sent home by which team after he went to a nightclub without permission?
18. Which team dyed their hair blonde?
19. Who were the first team to sack their coach during France '98?
20. Craig Burley was sent off when playing against which team?
21. Who was the first player to score a hat-trick?
22. Which three teams were knocked out of the tournament on penalties?
23. Who scored the winning goal for Romania against England?
24. Which country celebrated making their debut at the World Cup by finishing third?
25. Who scored the last goal of the tournament?

GENERAL KNOWLEDGE 1

1. The Gallagher brothers from Oasis support which football team?
2. Where are the Eclipse Stakes held?
3. What colour is the bullseye in archery?
4. How many pockets are there in Carom billiards?
5. Which female athlete became the first to win four Olympic gold medals in one games?
6. The Madejski stadium is the home of which football club?
7. Which woman won the Wimbledon singles title in 1971 aged 19?
8. Diane Moran is better known as which lycra-clad fitness freak?
9. 'Heaven Can Wait' is a film based around which sport?
10. Newmarket is in which county?
11. 'Ugly Inside' is a fanzine devoted to which southern football team?
12. The Cowdrey family played cricket for which county?
13. Which Steve won the BBC Sports Personality of the Year Award in 1983?
14. Which footballer earned the nickname 'the Lion of Vienna' for his performance in Austria in 1952?
15. Great Britain has appeared at every modern Summer Olympics. True or false?
16. The Orange Bowl is competed for in which sport?
17. Which country made its Test cricket debut in 1889?
18. In shinty, what is the Caman?
19. Which DJ was known for running marathons and fixing things?
20. The 1,000 Guineas is run over which distance: 1 mile, 2 miles or 3 miles?
21. 147lb is the top weight for which boxing division?
22. Tynecastle is the home ground of which Scottish football team?
23. The Wankhede cricket ground is in which city?
24. The first World Snooker Championship was held in which decade: the 1920's, 1930's or 1940's?
25. The Belmont Stakes is a horse race in which country?

MIXED BAG 23

1. In which year did England play the Rest of the World in an unofficial Test series for the Guinness Challenge?
2. Where is the St.Leger traditionally run?
3. Who was the captain of the 1978 World Cup winning team?
4. The 1984 Summer Olympics took place in which city?
5. Which American game is sometimes called the 'Game with no Clock'?
6. Noureddine Morceli is a runner from which country: Algeria, Morocco or Kenya?
7. Which spin bowler has the middle names Clive Roderick?
8. The 'Toon Army' support which football team?
9. Lord's is the home of which cricket county?
10. In snooker who is the 'Whirlwind'?
11. Tom Finney spent his entire football career at which club?
12. Which capital city hosted the 1952 Winter Olympics?
13. Which famous Henry was British Heavyweight Champion for eleven years?
14. Daniel Fonseca is a footballer from which country?
15. Glenn Hoddle left which club to manage England?
16. Which team lost in the 1934 World Cup final?
17. Which boxer changed his name by deed poll to 'Marvellous'?
18. How many balls are there in a game of billiards?
19. Does jockey Richard Dunwoody ride on the flat or in national hunt?
20. Which ex-Coventry, Sheffield Wednesday and Man Utd manager is now a football commentator?
21. Which Kiwi won the 1967 Formula One World Drivers' Championship?
22. Which country was first to win back-to-back World Cups?
23. Which well-known striker is known as 'Sparky'?
24. Ballyregan Bob is a famous name from which sport?
25. In tennis, which woman won the French Open in 1998?

FOOTBALL'S
FOREIGN LEGION

1. What nationality is Paulo Wanchope?
2. Man City signed Georgi Kinkladze from which club?
3. Who was the first overseas manager to win the FA Cup?
4. In which year did Spurs sign Ricardo Villa and Ossie Ardiles?
5. What is Juninho's first name?
6. Who replaced Ruud Gullit as manager of Chelsea?
7. Dennis Bergkamp is hoping to be a professional pilot once he leaves football. True or false?
8. Who was the first overseas manager to win the Premiership?
9. Had Jurgen Klinsmann not played football, he would have become a baker. True or false?
10. Which football club chairman called foreign footballers "Carlos Kickaball"?
11. Jurgen Klinsmann had two spells as a player at which London club?
12. Stig Bjornebye, Ole Gunnar Solskjaer and Lars Bohinen all come from which country?
13. Frank Leboeuf left which club for Chelsea?
14. Who replaced Walter Smith as manager of Rangers?
15. Who was the first black man to play in an FA Cup final?
16. Which Arsenal player was sent off and then cited for spitting at a fellow player in 1999?
17. Which manager bought a Senagalese striker called Ali Dia because he thought George Weah had phoned up and recommended him?
18. Which man said: "I wouldn't wash my car with his shirt now" about Jurgen Klinsmann?
19. Brian Laudrup left which club to go to Chelsea?
20. Which foreign Aston Villa player courted trouble when he spat at his own fans?
21. Dennis Bergkamp was named after which other football star?
22. Which Norwegian striker is known as the 'Baby-faced Assassin'?
23. Which Dutch player was described as looking like 'Bambi on Ice' during the 1998 World Cup?
24. "If I've upset or offended anybody, I'm very sorry." Which incident is the sportsman apologising for?
25. Which famous Man City goalkeeper was a former German POW?

EQUESTRIAN

1. Which ex-show jumper used to be a professional wrestler?
2. What is the first event in three-day eventing?
3. Which famous German rider was forced into retirement for alleged cruelty to his horses in 1990?
4. Blyth Tait is a rider from which country?
5. Which woman won Badminton in 1992?
6. Who won the BBC Sports Personality of the Year in 1971?
7. What three events make up Three Day Eventing?
8. 'V is for Victory' is a book by which show jumping legend?
9. The 1956 Olympics took place at Melbourne but in which city were the equestrian events held?
10. Who won Badminton in 1973 aged 20?
11. Hickstead is in which county?
12. Nelson Pesoa comes from which country?
13. In which year were sex tests introduced to the sport?
14. Who won Great Britain's only gold medal at the 1952 Olympics on Foxhunter?
15. Tatum O'Neal starred in the sequel to 'National Velvet'. What was it called?
16. Which Raymond was the founder of the Olympia Showjumping Championships?
17. Where would you find Luckington Lane?
18. Major Derek Alhusen won an Olympic gold aged 54 at which Olympics in the 60's?
19. David Broome's sister was also an accomplished rider. What is her name?
20. Nicola McIrvine won Badminton in 1990 on Middle Road. Which famous runner did she marry?
21. The first Hickstead Derby was held in which year of the 60's?
22. The World Equestrian Games took place at which city in 1998?
23. How often does the Royal International Horse Show take place?
24. Why did the equestrian events not take place in Melbourne during the 1956 Olympics?
25. The King George V Gold Cup is for male show jumpers only. True or false?

MIXED BAG 24

1. At which Olympics was the super heavyweight category first contested?
2. 'C'Mon Aussie C'Mon' was a hit in Australia. It was an anthem recorded to back their International rugby league team. True or false?
3. 'The Mag' is a fanzine from which football club?
4. Which exercise keeps your hands still on a step whilst you rotate your legs and body over it?
5. Is the Oaks a horse race for colts or fillies?
6. Name the Scottish football team who play at Fir Park?
7. 130lb is the top weight of which professional boxing weight?
8. Apart from skiing, what other Olympic sport would involve a piste?
9. In gymnastics the men's and women's horse vault are both the same length. True or false?
10. Which famous cricket almanac was first published in 1864?
11. Steve Elkington is a name from which sport?
12. Picabo Street is a skier from which country?
13. 1993 was the year the Grand National was declared void. Which horse won the race that never was?
14. Ronnie Irani is a cricketer from which county?
15. Which stretch and tone class is based on ballet?
16. In America, which sport is governed by the PRCA?
17. In 1964, Peru were trailing 1-0 with two minutes left when they had a goal disallowed. This decision caused a riot which led to 350 deaths. Which South American team were they playing?
18. At what age did Jennifer Capriati became a professional tennis player: 12, 13 or 14?
19. What nationality is the Jordan Formula One team supremo Eddie Jordan?
20. The 1908 Olympics was the first at which gold, silver and bronze medals were awarded. True or false?
21. Ezzard Charles is a name connected with which sport?
22. Which England cricketer is known as 'Freddy'?
23. Which major Australian sporting event happens every November on the first Tuesday?
24. In European football, what name is given to the trophy awarded to the top scorer in domestic league football?
25. Who retired from tennis in 1983 after he emerged from a Buddhist temple believing the Gods had released him from the game?

GRAND NATIONAL

1. Freddie Starr owned which National winner?
2. Red Rum won the National for the third time in which year?
3. How many times did Desert Orchid ride in the great race?
4. Who is called the 'First Lady of Aintree'?
5. In the history of the National who is Charlotte Brew?
6. How many times did Red Rum finish second?
7. The race was first televised live in which year: 1960, 1961 or 1962?
8. Is the Grand National run over 3½ or 4½ miles?
9. Jenny Pitman won the National for the first time with which horse?
10. Captain Beecher gave his name to which obstacle?
11. Which snail-like horse won in 1975?
12. Which horse set a record time by winning in 1990?
13. Which man won the National a year after being diagnosed with cancer?
14. Which rider won on Rough Quest and said later: "Sex is an anti-climax after that"?
15. Dick Saunders won the race in 1982 on Grittar. How old was he?
16. Peter Scudamore never won the National. True or false?
17. Which famous writer rode Devon Loch?
18. When was the first Grand National held at Aintree?
19. What was the horse called in the film 'National Velvet'?
20. How old was Red Rum when he won the National for the third time?
21. What is the youngest age at which a horse can compete in the National?
22. George Stevens holds the record for most race wins. How many times did he do it?
23. The site of which airport was the location for the National during the Second World War?
24. How many times did the horse 'Manifesto' run in the National?
25. What was the Grand National called when it was first run at Aintree?

GRAND PRIX

1. What was the name of Jacques Villeneuve's famous father?
2. What nationality is Pedro Diniz?
3. Which team were bought by Jaguar for the 2000 season?
4. "Schumacher is the fastest man on the track, he's gone around quicker than anyone else." Who said this?
5. Which man raced in 99 Grand Prix, won 27 of them and lifted three World Titles?
6. Which Grand Prix champion died in 1993 aged 45?
7. Who was the first man to win 50 Grand Prix in Formula One?
8. Guiseppe Farina did it in 1950 at the British Grand Prix and Giancarlo Baghetti did it in 1961 at the French Grand Prix. What did they achieve?
9. Nigel Mansell has played which other sport professionally?
10. How many times did Stirling Moss finish second in the World Championship?
11. The A1-Ring is a track in which country?
12. Who are the Tifosi?
13. "I'm not a superman and I'm not an idiot. I'm somewhere in between." Who said this?
14. Which Grand Prix Champion won the title posthumously in the early 1970's?
15. Who won the BBC Sports Personality of the Year in 1961?
16. Up until 1960 how many points was a Grand Prix win worth?
17. Which team is based at Woking in Surrey?
18. Which Australian won the world title in a car he built?
19. How many times was Nelson Piquet World Champion?
20. In which county is Brands Hatch?
21. In which year did Damon Hill make his Formula One debut?
22. Jim Clark made all his 72 starts for which team?
23. How many times was Alain Prost World Champion?
24. Until the mid-80's which track was used for the British Grand Prix?
25. Which Austrian crashed at the Nurburgring in 1976 and nearly lost his life?

MIXED BAG 25

1. Which city was the first to host the Summer Olympics twice?
2. Which paper anticipated the worst with the headline: "Ooh Aah Prisonaah"?
3. Which Sri Lankan bowler demolished the England batting line-up in the 1998 Oval Test?
4. What nationality is Marcelo Salas?
5. Ian Sproat was Minister for Sport in which party's Government?
6. What distance was Bob Beamon's long jump record achieved at the Mexico Olympics?
7. Which cricket county plays at Trent Bridge?
8. What sport do the Toronto Raptors play?
9. Bill McLaren is a commentator associated with which sport?
10. How many times has Brazil lost in a World Cup final?
11. A GA is what position in netball?
12. A game of billiards has how many red balls?
13. If France and Brazil had both lost their semi-finals at France '98 which two teams would have contested the final?
14. Where do the basketball team the 'Nuggets' come from?
15. In American Football, who are the 'Pats'?
16. Who became manager of the Republic of Ireland football team in 1986?
17. Oscar Swann won an Olympic title in 1920 aged 72 in what sport?
18. In boxing, what is a 'journeyman'?
19. Which famous Finn did the 5,000m and 10,000m double at both the 1972 and 1976 Olympics?
20. What is an eighth of a mile called in racing?
21. In golf, can you score an albatross on a par three?
22. What is the Eskimo word for canoe?
23. In football who are known as the 'Pensioners'?
24. Which race is the oldest of the five flat racing Classics?
25. Muhammed Ali directed these insults against whom: "I've seen him shadow boxing and the shadow won"?

HISTORY

1. Which event took place for the first time in 776BC?
2. Bushido means 'Way of the Warrior' and was a code followed by which warriors?
3. How did the Greek God Apollo accidentally kill his friend Hyacinthus?
4. Why did Henry VIII ban bowls?
5. In which year were the first rules of football drawn up?
6. On Christmas Day 1914, what game did German and British troops play in No Man's Land?
7. In 1971 which astronaut hit a golf ball on the moon with a six iron?
8. Which athlete upset Hitler by winning four gold medals at the 1936 Olympics?
9. Which Eddie made cricketing history when he discharged himself from hospital, having spent four days there, and returned to the Brisbane ground where he scored a match-winning 86 in the Bodyline series?
10. Which Roman Emperor once competed at the Olympics in a ten-horse chariot, and despite not winning, was still awarded victory?
11. The first European Athletics Championships took place in which decade?
12. Over 2,500 years ago, the Chinese played a game called Tsu Chu, a form of which very popular sport known today?
13. Americans claim that Abner Doubleday, a West Point cadet, invented which game in 1839?
14. In the 10th Century, Mexicans played a game called Pok-Ta-Pok which resembled which fast moving, high scoring ball game?
15. Who delayed his departure to fight the Spanish Armada until he had finished his game of bowls?
16. Name the Queen imprisoned in 1576 after her billiard table had been confiscated?
17. Which King was told about the Irish Rebellion in 1641 while he was playing golf?
18. An electronic scoreboard was first used for field events at which Olympics?
19. Which of Henry VIII's wives gave him a set of darts as a present?
20. Which sport was founded in 1895 at a meeting in a Huddersfield hotel?
21. Emily Davidson threw herself under the King's horse at which race in 1913?
22. What did Reginald Stanley Brooks give Test cricket in 1882?
23. When did the first recorded Sumo bout take place?
24. In 1953, Hungary became the first overseas team to beat England at Wembley. What was the score?
25. According to history, which martial art was founded by a Buddhist Monk: Ta Mo Karate, Kempo or Kung Fu?

OLYMPICS 1

1. The very first Olympics were part of a religious festival to honour which God?
2. What colour are the five Olympic rings?
3. And what do the five Olympic rings represent?
4. Stanislawa Walasiewicz won the women's 100m in 1932. What was unusual about her?
5. Why was Linford Christie disqualified from the Atlanta Olympics?
6. Who were the winners of the first Olympic football tournament in 1908?
7. Where did the Olympics of 1948 take place?
8. Who won Great Britain's only gold medal at the Atlanta Olympics?
9. Who were the two main athletes portrayed in the film 'Chariots of Fire'?
10. Vasili Alexyev won two gold medals in which sport?
11. In which park did a bomb explode in during the 1996 games?
12. At an Olympic swimming final, the slowest qualifier always swims in which lane?
13. At what games were photo-finish cameras used for the first time?
14. Which man made history by winning the 5,000m, 10,000m and the marathon at the Helsinki Games?
15. In Atlanta Josia Thugwane became South Africa's first gold medallist, what was his event?
16. At the 1976 Olympics, only one competitor was excused the compulsory sex test. Who was that competitor?
17. Women competed at the Olympics for the very first time in which year?
18. Who won the men's 200m breaststroke gold at the Seoul Olympics?
19. Which man lit the Olympic flame at Atlanta?
20. At which Olympics did Great Britain win 56 gold medals?
21. Who threw his gold medal in a Kentucky river after being refused service in a diner because of his colour?
22. Who was captain of the Great Britain women's athletics team at Barcelona?
23. American athletes did the Black Power salute at which Games?
24. In 1984 who won the women's javelin gold?
25. How many countries accepted invitations to the Seoul Olympics: 141, 151 or 161?

MIXED BAG 26

1. The first four World Cup finals were won by just two countries. Name them.
2. Which game use to be started by a 'bully'?
3. Which cricketer was called 'Beefy'?
4. 'Bull Durham' is a film based on which sport?
5. Dusty Hare played rugby union for England in which position?
6. In which year did Sir Matt Busby die?
7. Who managed Aston Villa to European Cup glory in 1982?
8. Who did Frank Bruno beat to become World Heavyweight Champion?
9. Which footballer was BBC Sports Personality of the Year in 1990?
10. In American Football where do the Falcons come from?
11. Which Stanley retired from first class football aged 50?
12. What is the lowest score that cannot be achieved with a single dart?
13. The Pittsburgh Pirates play which sport?
14. Who has the names Luis Nazario De Lima?
15. Andrea Parenti is an Olympic Champion in which sport?
16. Which team play in front of the Brian Clough Stand?
17. Jean Borotra played at Wimbledon in 1964, competing in the men's and mixed doubles. How old was he?
18. How many holes are played in a professional golf tournament?
19. Which cricket commentator was affectionately known as 'Johnners'?
20. In canoeing categories, what does 'K' stand for?
21. Which footballer famously suffered from stress during the 1998-99 season?
22. Who was the first black player to score a hat-trick for England?
23. Venice Beach is in which US state?
24. In rugby union, what position does the No 9 play?
25. The first European Athletics Championships took place in 1934, in which European city?

POLITICS

1. Who was supposed to have presented Jesse Owens with his 100 metre gold medal at the Berlin Olympics?
2. Why did the USA not go to the Moscow Olympics?
3. Bernard Tapie, the former French MP, was president of which football club until they found out about his dodgy dealings?
4. Which politician had a yacht called Morning Cloud?
5. Seb Coe was an MP for which political party?
6. In 1905, which American President demanded changes to the rules of American Football because he considered there were too many deaths?
7. An Australian MP sent which England cricketer a telegram in 1978 which read: "You have done for Australian cricket what the Boston Strangler did for door-to-door salesmen"?
8. Who was Britain's first Minister for Sport?
9. It is said that Formula One's Max Mosley would have preferred to have been an MP, but couldn't because of his notorious father. Who was his father?
10. Winston Churchill described which game as "an ineffectual attempt to direct an uncontrollable sphere into an inaccessible hole with instruments ill-adapted to the purpose"?
11. Pele was a minister of what in Brazil?
12. John Major supports which football team?
13. Which two athletes did Black Power salutes on the podium at the Mexico Olympics, during the 200m medal ceremony?
14. On being appointed Minister of Sport, who said: "It's a bit like going to heaven without having to die first"?
15. Party Politics was the Grand National winner in which election year?
16. Eastern Bloc countries (Romania apart) staged a boycott of which Olympics on the pretext that the safety of their athletes could not be guaranteed?
17. Which England cricket captain opposed James Callaghan at the 1964 General Election?
18. Which Pakistan captain retired from cricket to go into politics?
19. Which famous sportsman was MP for Falmouth and Cambourne until 1997?
20. Ex-MP Cyril Smith was a British marathon runner in his youth. True or false?
21. Which squad in Euro '96 was allowed to fax their votes back home as they had a General Election?
22. Black African athletes stayed away from which Olympics because of New Zealand's continuing sporting links with South Africa?
23. Bob Mathias, who won the Olympic decathlon titles in 1948 and 1952, went on to become a politician in which country?
24. What was the original nationality of Kitei Son (real name Sohn Kee-Chung) who won the 1936 Olympic marathon, having been forced to run for Japan?
25. Why was Graham Gooch banned from playing Test cricket for three years?

RELIGION

1. In 1977 which famous heavyweight retired to become a preacher?
2. Sumo has its origins in which religion?
3. Which player did Rangers sign from Nantes in 1989?
4. Which sport did David Sheppard leave to dedicate his life to God?
5. To which religion did Henry Cooper convert in order to marry his wife?
6. Which man said he wouldn't run on a Sunday in the 1924 Olympics and went on to become a missionary?
7. Thai boxing has links with which religion?
8. Which football club was founded as Christ Church?
9. Rugby player Michael Jones refuses to play on Sundays. Which country does he play for?
10. Who are Southampton supporters praising when they talk about 'Le God'?
11. In 1998 which Premiership rugby union club advertised itself with the slogan 'The Unholy Trinity', deemed blasphemous by some members of the clergy?
12. Which devout Christian won the triple jump at the 1998 European Athletics Championships?
13. In the NFL, where do the Saints come from?
14. Who was Cyril Knowles' brother who gave up professional football to become a Jehovah's Witness?
15. Which former Coventry goalie was labelled the 'Son of God' by the media?
16. Christian Cullen is a name associated with which sport?
17. Which Scottish football team is mentioned in the Bible?
18. Pope John Paul II blessed the World Cup for which tournament?
19. In which golf Major would you find 'Amen Corner'?
20. Pope John Paul II has an autograph of which Welsh striker in the Vatican?
21. Larry Nelson, a born-again Christian, plays which sport?
22. Moses Tanui is a runner from which country?
23. Which football club released a record called 'Onward Sexton's Soldiers'?
24. Which New Zealand snooker player had his own guru?
25. Which Henry was World Boxing Champion at three different weights and became a Baptist Minister in 1951?

MIXED BAG 27

1. Darren Peacock left Newcastle Utd for which club in 1998?
2. At which cricket ground would you find the Radcliffe Road End?
3. The 'Brumbrella' is associated with which sport?
4. Jackie Joyner-Kersee was a World record holder in which jumping event?
5. Brian Gamlin created the scoring system for which sport in 1896?
6. 'The Tricky Tree' is a fanzine devoted to which football club?
7. 'Goal' was a documentary about which World Cup?
8. In American Football the Redskins come from which city?
9. What does EPRUC stand for?
10. The man who invented basketball was Canadian. True or false?
11. What nationality is the footballer George Weah?
12. How long is the break in between boxing rounds?
13. Sachin Tendulkar plays cricket for which country?
14. The Nurburgring track stages which Grand Prix?
15. In which joint would you find your cruciate ligament?
16. Who was England rugby union coach before Clive Woodward?
17. Nathan Astle plays Test cricket for which country?
18. 'South of the Border' is a term for what in boxing?
19. Which country hosted the 1962 World Cup Finals?
20. Doug Mountjoy was a snooker player from which country?
21. The Doncaster Belles are a top team in which sport?
22. Alex Murphy is regarded as one of the greatest-ever players in which sport?
23. 'Pumping Iron' is a film starring whom?
24. In which year did Harry Redknapp become West Ham manager?
25. Where did Tom Watson win the first of his five British Opens?

WOMEN'S TENNIS

1. Which woman defected at the American Open in 1975?
2. Who won the Wimbledon Singles title in the Queen's Silver Jubilee year?
3. What nationality is Martina Hingis?
4. Who was the first woman to complete the Grand Slam of all four tennis Major titles in one year?
5. Which Brazilian woman won Wimbledon in 1959, 1960 and 1964?
6. How many times has Gabriella Sabatini won Wimbledon?
7. Sue Barker used to go out with which musical God?
8. Which 16-year-old won the US Open in 1979?
9. How did Gunther Parache attain notoriety?
10. Who was once attacked by a mugger on a Detroit escalator but managed to fend him off with her tennis racket?
11. Name the player who was called 'Little Mo'?
12. How many Grand Slam singles titles did Jo Durie win?
13. Who won the BBC Sports Personality of the Year in 1977?
14. In 1982 who succeeded Virginia Wade as British No 1?
15. Which woman was named 1994 Sports Presenter of the Year?
16. Who did Jo Durie win the Wimbledon Mixed Doubles with?
17. Before Martina Navratilova became American what nationality was she?
18. Which British tennis player did Chris Evert marry?
19. In 1978 which woman won the Wimbledon Singles title for the first time?
20. Which 55-year-old man challenged Billie-Jean King to a famous battle of the sexes tennis match?
21. At the 1992 Olympics which woman won the singles title?
22. Mirjana Lucic is a female tennis star from which country?
23. Charlotte Cooper was the first woman to win Olympic tennis gold at which Olympics: 1900, 1904 or 1908?
24. Britain play which other country for the Wightman Cup?
25. How many Wimbledon Singles titles did Chris Evert win: 3, 4 or 5?

BOXING HEAVIES 2

1. When Lennox Lewis won the super heavyweight Olympic gold medal, who did he beat in the final?
2. Riddick Bowe chucked which belt in the bin?
3. Who is the only man to have won three successive Olympic heavyweight boxing titles?
4. Who was heavyweight World Champion from 1908 to1915?
5. In 1982 Michael Dokes beat whom in 63 seconds, making it the shortest ever World heavyweight title bout?
6. How old was Joe Bugner when he became the oldest man to win a heavyweight title by beating James Smith for the WBF title in 1998?
7. Which miraculous boxer fought Ali in 1962 a few weeks short of his 49th birthday?
8. Which slaughterman from South Carolina went on to become World Heavyweight Champion?
9. In which year did Mike Tyson first become World Champion?
10. Who was the first English born boxer to win the World heavyweight title?
11. Larry Holmes fought which man who had been tagged the 'Great White Hope' by the American media?
12. Which British heavyweight has the nickname of the 'Zulu Warrior'?
13. Mike Tyson defeated which Olympic gold medallist in 91 seconds?
14. Who defeated Joe Frazier in 1973 in Kingston, Jamaica to become World Champion?
15. Who was known as the 'Easton Assassin'?
16. Tommy Morrison had a part in which Rocky Film?
17. Which World Heavyweight Champion was known as 'Terrible Tim'?
18. Which famous heavyweight died on 31st August 1969?
19. Which boxer said: "Marciano couldn't carry my jockstrap"?
20. Floyd Patterson didn't win his Olympic gold medal at heavyweight. At which weight did he win it?
21. Francesco Damiani is a heavyweight champion from which country?
22. How many world title fights did Joe Louis have?
23. At 5ft 7in, which Canadian was the shortest World Heavyweight Champion?
24. When Bob Fitzimmons became World Heavyweight Champion how heavy was he?
25. Which man said this in reference to Ali: "I can't tell no jokes and I don't write no poems but I'm the best in the world at knocking people down"?

COACHES

1. Barry Switzer is a coach from which sport?
2. Who was Red Rum's trainer?
3. Tomislav Ivic was sacked three weeks before France '98 as coach of which team?
4. Which Scot was Glenn Hoddle's assistant in the England job?
5. Which Argentina coach resigned after being knocked out of France '98?
6. Which actor played the bobsleigh coach in the film 'Cool Runnings'?
7. Graham Henry became coach of which rugby union nation in 1998?
8. Henry Cecil is a name connected with which sport?
9. Who succeeded Jack Charlton as coach of the Republic of Ireland?
10. Who did Ian McGeechan succeed as Scotland rugby union coach?
11. Which former England batsman and coach is called 'Bumble'?
12. In 1998 which Australian was appointed Director of Rugby at Bristol?
13. David Leadbetter is a guru from which sport?
14. Which former British sprinting great is now Darren Campbell's coach?
15. Who was the coach of Scotland during France '98?
16. Kevin Cadle and Mike Finger are both coaches in which sport?
17. Bobby Robson became the coach of which Premiership team in 1999?
18. Gus D'Amato discovered which heavyweight champ?
19. In 1998 who was announced as the new St.Helens coach?
20. Dan Topolski coached which Boat Race team in the 1980's?
21. Which TV commentator also coached Lynn Davis?
22. 'Coach' is a TV show about which sport?
23. Who was England rugby union coach before Clive Woodward?
24. Which John coached Wigan and brought fifteen trophies to Central Park?
25. Scotland rugby union coach Ian McGeechan was born in England. True or false?

MIXED BAG 28

1. The film 'The Fan' is based on which sport?
2. Which country had a France '98 song called 'Rise Up'?
3. Jesper Parnevik is a golfer from which country?
4. In which city is Headingley cricket ground?
5. Who won the 1998 Sports Personality of the Year Award?
6. Which sport is also called gridiron?
7. Which cricket commentator is known as the 'Boil'?
8. 'The Fighting Marine' was the nickname of which boxer?
9. In which position did Fran Cotton play rugby union for England?
10. Who plays at Blundell Park?
11. The Cleveland Indians play which sport?
12. In which game can a player score a ringer, a gater or a black spot?
13. Jack Russell plays cricket for which county?
14. When England won the 1966 World Cup, who wore number 10?
15. Which Irishman trained the famous Triple Crown winner Nijinsky in 1970?
16. When England won the Five Nations Grand Slam in 1980, who was the captain?
17. Who was the first spin bowler to take 300 Test wickets?
18. Alain Robidoux is a Canadian associated with which sport?
19. Silly point is a position in which sport?
20. Which football club plays at Filbert Street?
21. Which John holds the NBA all-time record for the most assists?
22. Oscar De La Hoya won his Olympic Boxing Gold at which Games?
23. In the Five Nations, can France win the Triple Crown?
24. Which man won the British Open aged 46 years 99 days?
25. How many muscles make up your tricep?

WRESTLING

1. Klondike Kate is a wrestler from which country?
2. What was Big Daddy's real name?
3. Who played Bomber in 'Auf Weidershen Pet'?
4. Which deceased actor and wrestler was the voice of Tetley Tea?
5. Who had the catchphrase: "Not the ears, not the ears"?
6. Which wrestler said this: "They see a powerful, dominant and attractive man who can't be pushed around by anybody... everything that their husbands aren't. But in turn they don't want to make their feelings obvious – so they slag me off."
7. Whose wife said: "He doesn't fit into the bath, we hose him down in the garden."
8. Sir Jimmy Savile was once a wrestler. True or false?
9. Harvey Smith left wrestling for which other sport?
10. In sumo what is a 'Rikishi'?
11. Who once fought under the name of the 'Blonde Adonis'?
12. In which film does Sylvester Stallone persuade his brother to wrestle?
13. How was Luke McMasters better known?
14. In wrestling what is a ring rat?
15. What is the WWF?
16. Which bad boy of basketball with his freaky hair and tattoos has been involved in American wrestling?
17. How was Peter Thornley better known?
18. What is a Doyo in sumo?
19. What is a sumo tournament called?
20. How is Rodzilla better known?
21. Ken Richmond was always seen in J Arthur Rank films, what did he do?
22. What is the 'face' in wrestling?
23. Can you use your legs in Greco-Roman wrestling?
24. How many days does a sumo tournament last?
25. Who was Big Daddy's biggest adversary?

UNUSUAL SPORTS

1. The 'Marathon des Sable' takes place across 143 miles of which desert?
2. Mad Maurice from Melksham has been a world champion in which sport?
3. Which event features a 38km swim, 1800km cycle and a 420km run?
4. Which organisation is credited with inventing bungee jumping?
5. The first prize in the national rattlesnake championship of America is decided by the first person to do what?
6. Paul Vjestica became the 33rd World Champion in which sport?
7. Calico Storico is a game involving teams of 27 fighting over a ball be chucked around in a net. With which country would you associate it?
8. The World Haggis Hurling Championship takes place every August. True or false?
9. Which Argentine game features teams of four horseman who throw a ball with six leather handles?
10. In the Afghan game of Buzkashi: which animal is slaughtered, filled with sand and then thrown about?
11. How is 'Octopush' otherwise known?
12. What was invented in 1973 by a group of drinkers at a pub in West Sussex?
13. In 1980 an official was knocked out whilst measuring in the WHHC. What does the acronym stand for?
14. Nicholas Andriakopoulos won which event at the 1896 Olympics?
15. Sticking with the Olympics, in 1900 which event was won with a distance of 188.4 metres?
16. Live pigeon shooting was once an Olympic event. True or false?
17. In 1982 Scott Weiland ran the Detroit Marathon in 4 hours, 7 minutes, 53 seconds. What was different about it?
18. Devonport, Portsmouth and Fleet Air Arm all compete in which race?
19. How many players make up a bicycle polo team: 4, 5 or 6?
20. In 1867 in Plymouth, the Ugly Men played the Handsome Men at which sport?
21. Zak Phillips created which sport?
22. Launceston Elliott won which Olympic title in 1896 with a lift of 71kg?
23. To raise money for the 1980 Olympics, Daley Thompson raced a greyhound. True or false?
24. In the 1970's, which famous Australian fast bowler attempted to get into the Guinness Book of Records by beating the egg-throwing record?
25. In 1961 the British Champions beat a Commonwealth team on the top of Mount Kilamanjaro at which game?

MIXED BAG 29

1. Christopher Martin-Jenkins commentates and writes about which sport?
2. In which year did Italy first host the football World Cup Finals?
3. What sport is played on a diamond?
4. Who was the first cricketer to win BBC Sports Personality of the Year?
5. In American Football where do the Giants and the Jets come from?
6. Which footballer was the subject of the first ever £1,000 transfer?
7. Can there be a draw in amateur boxing?
8. Tatum O'Neal was married to which tennis star?
9. In basketball what is a 'double team'?
10. Who won the 1980 Olympic 100m title coached by his wife?
11. How many Tests did Sri Lanka play in England in 1998?
12. Which Indian batsman became Yorkshire's first overseas player?
13. In pool what is a 'Michael Caine'?
14. 'The Great White Hype' is a film based on which sport?
15. Which Premiership team play at St James's Park?
16. How many rounds did the second Bruno/Tyson fight last?
17. No21 was the shirt number of which England player in the 1966 World Cup final?
18. Which rugby union team play at Heywood Road?
19. 'Heroes & Villains' is a fanzine devoted to which football club?
20. Which team won the 1998 Benson & Hedges Cup final?
21. In boxing what is 'showboating'?
22. '4' and '5' are the positional numbers of which players in rugby union?
23. In golf what is a 'Big Bertha'?
24. Carlos Moya is a tennis player from which country?
25. Who did Lennox Lewis beat to win his first World heavyweight title?

MIDDLE DISTANCE

1. Which athlete won BBC Sports Personality of the Year first: Steve Ovett or Seb Coe?
2. The women's 1500m was run first at which Olympics?
3. Which football team does Steve Cram support?
4. Who was the first man to break 3 minutes 50 for the mile?
5. Which Sheffield steel worker won 1500m silver at the 1988 Olympics?
6. Before Zola Budd became British what nationality was she?
7. In the decathlon the men complete the event with the 1500m. What distance do the women run to end the heptathlon?
8. Between 1954 and 1960 which Australian remained undefeated for 44 races at both the mile and 1500m distances?
9. In which city did Roger Bannister break the four-minute barrier for the mile?
10. Albert Hill won the 800m and 1500m for Great Britain at which Olympics?
11. How many water jumps do you have to hurdle in a 3,000 metre steeplechase?
12. Who was the second man to run a four-minute mile?
13. When was the women's 3,000m first run at the Olympics?
14. Sebastian Coe was named after a character from which Shakespeare play?
15. In the 1984 Olympics this man won the 5000m gold but didn't run the 1500m because of the timetable. He later claimed: "If I'd run in the 1500m I'd have won that. Seb is a champion by default." Who is he?
16. What nationality is John Walker?
17. After winning the 800m in the 1980 Olympics which man spelt I LY (I Love You) in the air?
18. Which Russian woman won the 800m and 1500m at the Atlanta Olympics?
19. Why was John Mayock booed when he won the 3000m at the European Indoor Athletics Championship in Valencia in 1998?
20. She came to British athletics under something of a cloud. She was later called Mrs Pieterse. Who is she?
21. When Roger Bannister broke the 4-minute mile who was the pacesetter he nicknamed the 'Red Fox'?
22. What is the last event in the heptathlon?
23. Which famous World record took place in 1954 on 6th May?
24. Chris Chataway was an MP for which party?
25. The first woman to run the mile in less than five minutes was British. What was her name?

OVERSEAS FOOTBALL

1. Juventus come from which Italian city?
2. Which country won the men's football gold medal the Atlanta Olympics?
3. In November 1980 Liberia played out a 0-0 draw with Gambia but what would would the consequences have been if they had lost?
4. Which Portuguese player had the nicknames the 'Black Pearl' and the 'Black Panther'?
5. Born in Brazil, Luis Oliveria played his national football for which country?
6. Boca Juniors are a well-known team from which country?
7. Who was born Manuel Francisco Dos Santos?
8. Which American came to our attention because he looked like Catweasel, had big ginger hair and a ginger goatee?
9. Who won the Champions League in 1998?
10. Which Portuguese side plays at the Stadium of Light?
11. All these football grounds are in which country: Stade Constant Vaden Stock, Stade Joseph Marien and Olympiastadion?
12. Rats played in the World Cup for which team?
13. Which Italian is called the 'Divine Ponytail'?
14. Who is regarded as the greatest-ever Dutch footballer, scoring 33 goals in 44 International appearances?
15. Roy Hodgson used to coach which European national side?
16. Colombian footballer Carlos Valderrama's unusual appearance sets him apart from other players. What is his distinctive feature?
17. Barcelona play their home football matches at which ground?
18. Honved are a football club from which country?
19. After leaving the England job, which Dutch team did Bobby Robson manage?
20. Name the famous striking duo for Real Madrid in the early 60's?
21. Dalymount Park is the home of which Irish football team?
22. Which Italian football team come from Sardinia?
23. The NASL was started in America in the 1970's. What was it?
24. In 1972 an entire football team was tried and imprisoned after a linesman was kicked to death in which South American country?
25. Which German striker trained to be an Opera singer before deciding on football?

MIXED BAG 30

1. Which country won the World Cup first: Germany or Brazil?
2. In rugby union what is the IRB?
3. The Holte End is at which football ground?
4. Which cricket commentator has the nickname 'Blowers'?
5. The Japanese Grand Prix takes place at which track?
6. Which British man won the 100m European Athletic Championship title in 1998?
7. Brazil won the World Cup in 1958. Who did they beat in the final?
8. Mickey Mantle is a legend in which sport?
9. Aravinda De Silva is a World-class batsman for which Test side?
10. In Super League who are the 'Warriors'?
11. 'Bowls on Ice' is a description of which game?
12. When the British Lions toured Australia in 1989, who was their captain?
13. Which sport has a governing body called FITA?
14. How many counties competed in the first county cricket championship: 9, 10 or 11?
15. Jemima Goldsmith is married to which sportsman?
16. In netball what position is GA?
17. What is the person who throws the ball in baseball called?
18. Freestyle and Greco-Roman are two styles of which sport?
19. FITA is the controlling body of which sport?
20. Who won the US Masters in 1998?
21. Do you have line-outs in rugby league?
22. Which number is between 18 and 13 on a dartboard?
23. 'White Love' is a fanzine written by the supporters of which football club?
24. Which type of cross-country running involves much steeper and frequently longer courses and is normally confined to highland areas of Britain?
25. Which future England captain was an apprentice at Manchester United but was released to Crewe Alexandra on a free transfer?

FA CUP 2

1. How many times did Liverpool win the FA Cup in the 80's?
2. Which London team won the 1982 FA Cup final?
3. Which ground hosted the final the year before the first Wembley game?
4. In 1890 William Towley became the first man to do what in an FA Cup final?
5. In the 80's Brighton lost to which team in an FA Cup final?
6. Which club won the first FA Cup final at Wembley?
7. Ipswich won the FA Cup in which year: 1977, 1978 or 1979?
8. What was unusual about the winners of the 1911 FA Cup?
9. Who are the only non-league team to win the FA Cup in the 20th Century?
10. Which was the first FA Cup final replay staged at Wembley?
11. What have Mark Crossley and Dave Beasant got in common?
12. Name the substitutes who both scored twice in the 1989 all-Merseyside final?
13. Who were the last Second Division side in the 20th Century to win the FA Cup?
14. Who won the Centenary FA Cup final?
15. Which northern team were awarded the trophy following their third successive win in 1886?
16. Which team was the first to achieve the League and Cup double?
17. Who scored three goals in the 'Matthews Final' of 1953?
18. Which referee sent-off Kevin Moran in the 1985 FA Cup final?
19. In what year of the 80's did Watford lose in the FA Cup final?
20. In 1990 which 'keeper replaced Jim Leighton in the FA Cup final replay?
21. Name the team that won the Scottish FA Cup four times in the 80's?
22. Which 'keeper broke his neck in the 1956 FA Cup final yet stayed on the field and helped his team to victory?
23. In reaching the 1998 FA Cup final Newcastle had to struggle against which Vauxhall Conference side?
24. Man Utd announced they would not be entering the 1999-2000 FA Cup because they were due to play in a tournament in which country?
25. Which club won its first and only trophy of the 20th Century in 1987?

COMMENTATORS

1. In 1946 which commentator said in the boat race: "Oxford are ahead, no Cambridge are ahead. I don't know who's ahead but it's either Oxford or Cambridge."
2. Which rugby league commentator was famous for saying "Up n'under"?
3. Which Radio Five Live commentator said: "Martin Keown's up everyone's backside"?
4. Name the former MP who chaired the Football Task Force and the phone-in '606' on Radio Five Live?
5. At the 1976 Olympics which man was the only member of the British track and field team to win a medal?
6. Which man is known as 'Blowers'?
7. Which BBC pundit said, after Man Utd lost on the opening day of the season: "You'll never win anything with kids"?
8. Jonathan Agnew described how Ian Botham hit his own stumps by saying: "He couldn't get his leg over". This in turn made his co-commentator laugh himself silly. Who was he?
9. For which sport was commentator Dave Marr, who died in 1997, best known?
10. Which Channel Four commentator gave evidence in defence of Sporting Life in the 1998 Ramsden libel trial?
11. Who is the James who hosts Gazzetta Football Italia?
12. Which Sky football commentator advertised Snickers during France '98?
13. Who is the larger-than-life Channel Four racing pundit famous for exuberant hats?
14. Ray French is described as the voice of which sport?
15. Peter Jones died in 1990 while commentating on which famous event?
16. Which commentator said: "The bowler's Holding, the batsman's Willey."
17. Who said: "I make no apologies for their absence but I'm sorry they're not here"?
18. Which former BBC pundit is known for his chin?
19. Who is 'Motty'?
20. Sid Waddell is a name normally associated with which sport?
21. Which football team does Sky Sports presenter Helen Chamberlain support?
22. Mark Nicholas commentates on which sport?
23. Which well-respected coach and commentator inspired Lynn Davies to his Olympic Gold in 1964?
24. Which cricket commentator had a book published in 1998 called 'Anything But An Autobiography'?
25. Grandstand presenter Ray Stubbs was a former professional in which sport?

MIXED BAG 31

1. What nationality is Willie Shoemaker?
2. The England cricketer Robin Smith was born in which country?
3. Which city do the gridiron team the Chiefs come from?
4. From which island does Matt Le Tissier come?
5. In which sport do you have the clean and jerk?
6. Which football team plays its home matches at Upton Park?
7. Yorkshire competed in cricket's first County Championship: True or false?
8. Madonna used to date which bad boy of basketball?
9. The film 'The Club' is a humorous look at which sport?
10. Who did Australia beat in the final to win the 1987 Cricket World Cup?
11. A linebacker is a position in which sport?
12. Ricardo Lopez is a former Straw-weight Champion from which country?
13. What does NBA stand for?
14. Whom did Jamie Redknapp marry in 1998?
15. 'The Hornets' is a nickname for which football team?
16. Which number is between '13' and '10' on a dartboard?
17. How often are the Winter Olympics held?
18. WA is what position in netball?
19. Which sport is for individuals or teams, in which you compete on foot across rough country, heading for control points by use of a map and a compass?
20. Who won golf's US Open in 1994?
21. Robert Croft plays cricket for which county?
22. In rugby league, players in which position wear the No1 jersey?
23. Lottie Dodd left tennis aged twenty-one to take up which other sport?
24. 'The Way of Harmony and Spirit' is a translation of which martial art?
25. Who wore the No 9 shirt for England in the 1966 World Cup final?

TEST CRICKET

1. Who succeeded Alec Stewart as England captain in 1999?
2. In 1975 which cricket ground was sabotaged after supporters of a convict protested his innocence by digging up the pitch?
3. What does the WG in WG Grace stand for?
4. Brian Lara holds the record for the highest Test score. What is it?
5. Which England cricket captain invited a barmaid up to his room for a drink and lost the captaincy as a result?
6. Michael Atherton made his Test debut in which year?
7. What was the score in England's Test series in the West Indies in 1998?
8. Which Test side wear the baggy green cap?
9. In 1981 which England captain was described as a cross between Freud and Merlin?
10. Name the fast bowler who refused to bowl bodyline in that infamous series and went on to captain England?
11. 'Whispering Death' was the nickname of which great fast bowler?
12. Who in 1998 was caught on camera giving a 'V' sign to Philo Wallace after he was out lbw to Dean Headley in the fifth Test?
13. In 1938, who scored a then World record 364 against Australia?
14. Who was the first Test cricketer to score 5,000 runs, take 350 wickets and 100 catches?
15. When Dennis Lillee met the Queen in 1977 what did her ask her for?
16. Who played cricket for England aged 52 years and 165 days?
17. Which Sussex captain was out for a duck on his Test debut against the West Indies in 1995?
18. When South Africa toured in 1998, who was their captain?
19. Who is England's all time leading Test wicket-taker?
20. Who was the first player to be knighted during his cricket career?
21. Who played 125 Tests for India between 1971 and 1987?
22. Which country boy from Bowral became the world's best batsman?
23. Which cousin of Clive Lloyd took 309 wickets for the West Indies?
24. Which team had its first Test in 1982: Sri Lanka, Zimbabwe or Holland
25. Dominic Cork took a hat-trick for England against the West Indies in 1995. Who was the last Englishman before him to achieve the feat?

WIMBLEDON

1. In 1981, who famously said: "You guys are the absolute pits of the world"?
2. When Goran Ivanisevic lost in the 1998 Men's singles final, how many finals had he lost?
3. The tie-break was first introduced to the tournament in which year?
4. Fred Perry was the last Englishman to win the Wimbledon singles title in which year?
5. What was unusual about Ted Schraeder's appearance in the 1949 tournament?
6. Bjorn Borg won the Wimbledon title for the last time in 1980: True or false?
7. Before 1998 Jana Novotna had lost in two finals to which two players?
8. In the history of Wimbledon, who is Spencer William Gore?
9. Who in 1998 ended the five-year reign of Todd Woodbridge and Mark Woodforde?
10. Which French woman lost in the 1998 Wimbledon singles final?
11. How old was Lottie Odd when she won Wimbledon in 1887?
12. Men receive a cup for winning the title, what do women receive?
13. When was the first TV transmission of Wimbledon?
14. Which singer entertained the Wimbledon crowd when it rained?
15. When was the first Wimbledon Championship held?
16. In 1920 who was the first American man to win to win the singles title?
17. Adrian Hayden was one of Britain's best table tennis players. Who was his Wimbledon-winning daughter?
18. Gussie Moran was the first woman to show what at Wimbledon in 1949?
19. In 1983 who did John McEnroe beat 6-2, 6-2, 6-2 in the final?
20. Which woman first won the singles title in 1971 and then in 1980?
21. Men were first tested for drugs in which year?
22. Women were first tested for drugs in which year?
23. In 1975 Arthur Ashe won the title, but which man did he beat in the final who was at the time suing him for $2 million?
24. In 1907 Norman Brookes became the first overseas man to win the singles title. What nationality was he?
25. Which British player was thrown out of Wimbledon in 1995 after he smashed a ball in anger and accidentally hit a ball-girl?

MIXED BAG 32

1. In which part of your body are your quadriceps?
2. Alex Zulle is a cyclist from which country?
3. In the NBA, the Pacers come from which city?
4. In which city were the 1904 Summer Olympics held?
5. Which 24-year-old book assistant from Petersfield became a Tabloid sensation following a streak at Twickenham?
6. What was Michael Jordan's shirt number?
7. Which resort was the first to hold the Winter Olympics twice?
8. Which famous British Formula One World Champion died at Hockenheim in 1968?
9. Heather Small is associated with which rugby league player?
10. Who won the 1982 World Cup?
11. In Super League, who are the 'Wolves'?
12. 'North Dallas 40' is a film about which sport?
13. Ian Black was the first person from which sport to win BBC Sports Personality of the Year?
14. Which American Football team used to play at Foxboro stadium?
15. In baseball, the Cubs and the White Sox come from which city?
16. Who was England's captain at France '98?
17. Which man won twelve tennis Grand Slams in the 1960's?
18. Which numbers are either side of '3' on a dartboard?
19. Adi Dassler founded adidas. Which sportswear company was started by his brother Rudi Dassler?
20. How many people make up a team in hurling?
21. What game is softball derived from?
22. Which two counties shared cricket's County Championship in 1977?
23. Willie Mays is a name associated with which sport?
24. Which England football captain was accused of stealing a bracelet?
25. When Scotland won the Five Nations Grand Slam in 1990, who was the captain?

OLYMPICS 2

1. The Olympics motto is 'Citius, Altius, Fortius' what does it mean?
2. Which city hosted the Summer Olympics in 1968?
3. Which woman smashed the 100m world record at the 1988 Olympics?
4. Grace Kelly's father won three gold medals in which event?
5. Who was the founder of the modern Olympics?
6. How many countries took part at the 1900 Olympics: 20, 22 or 24?
7. Paavro Nurmi won five athletic golds at which Olympics?
8. If you won an event at the 1896 Games, what colour medal did you get?
9. In how many Olympics did Tessa Sanderson compete?
10. Why is Richard Jewell synonymous with the Atlanta Olympics?
11. Who won the first Gold medal awarded in baseball at the 1992 Olympics?
12. Ann Holdman became the first woman to win a track event in a heat at which Olympics?
13. A torch was first carried from Olympus to the games in which year?
14. What does IOC stand for?
15. USSR sent their first team to which Olympics?
16. Which colour medal did Jonathan Edwards win at the Atlanta Olympics?
17. Lucy Morton was the first woman to win an Olympic swimming title. At which Games did she achieve this?
18. Which Cuban former basketball player was the sensation of the 1976 Olympics by becoming the first to win both the 400m and 800m?
19. The women of Ancient Greece were banned from watching or competing in the early Olympics. The penalty for doing this was death. True or false?
20. In which event did Al Oerter win four consecutive titles between 1956 and 1968?
21. In the first modern Olympics, how many countries competed: 8, 10 or 12?
22. Women had their own games in Ancient Greece named after whose wife?
23. John Ljunggren won the gold in 1948 with a time of 4.41.52, he was third in 1956 with 4.35.02 and second in 1960 with 4.25.47. What was the event?
24. Women's track and field events were introduced at which games?
25. How old was Linford Christie when he won the Olympic gold?

Answers to WIMBLEDON

1. John McEnroe 2. Three 3. 1971 4. 1936 5. He played with a pipe in his mouth 6. True 7. Steffi Graf and Martina Hingis 8. The first-ever male winner 9. Jacco Eltingh and Paul Haarhuis 10. Natalie Tauziat 11. Fifteen 12. A plate 13. 1937 14. Cliff Richard 15. 1871 16. Bill Tilden 17. Ann Jones 18. Her Underwear 19. Chris Lewis 20. Evonne Cawley 21. 1986 22. 1990 23. Jimmy Connors 24. Australian 25. Tim Henman

FIRSTS 2

1. When were light meters first introduced to Test cricket: 1976, 1977 or 1978?
2. Liselott Linsenhoff was the first woman to win an Olympic title competing against men. What was the event?
3. Which fiery character was the first Test cricketer to take 300 wickets?
4. James Connolly became the first to do what in 1896?
5. Which country was the first to host the World Cup Finals twice?
6. Who was the first woman to hit a six in a Test Match?
7. Who were the two men who fought for the first World Heavyweight Championship under Queensbury Rules?
8. Charles Bannerman achieved the first what in Test Cricket?
9. Which woman became the first to climb the Matterhorn?
10. Who was the first man to take Mike Tyson the distance in his professional career?
11. Test cricket first started in which year?
12. Against Yugoslavia in 1968, who became the first England footballer to be sent off?
13. Which famous horserace was first held in 1920?
14. WG Grace was the first to score 100 first-class centuries. True or false?
15. Which Englishman was the first to win the US Golf Open?
16. Who was the first footballer to receive a knighthood?
17. Who was the first woman to be granted a licence to box professionally in this country?
18. Who was the first English born heavyweight World Champion?
19. Which England wicket-keeper became the first to achieve 200 dismissals and score 4,000 runs in Test cricket?
20. Alex Greaves was the first woman to ride in which Classic?
21. In 1956, who became the first Englishman to be named European Footballer of the Year?
22. Entry Badge was the first winner of which race?
23. Which famous golf tournament took place for the first time on 4th October 1895 at Newport, Rhode Island?
24. Name the first English football team to win what is now known as the UEFA Cup?
25. Who was the first cricketer to win one hundred Test caps?

MIXED BAG 33

1. Who won the 1990 Grand National?
2. In which year did Brazil first win the World Cup?
3. 'Semi Tough' is a film about which sport?
4. The Hungarian Grand Prix takes place at which track?
5. In rugby union what number is usually worn by the fly-half?
6. Who was the first footballer to win BBC Sports Personality of the Year?
7. In American Football how many points do you receive for a touchdown?
8. Who were the first English team to win the European Cup?
9. Steve Sampson was sacked as coach of which team at France '98?
10. To which country did Harold Larwood surprisingly emigrate?
11. The Veuve Cliquot Gold Cup is awarded in which sport?
12. What was Pele's shirt number for Brazil?
13. Where were the 1992 Winter Olympics held?
14. Which actor starred in the film 'The Natural'?
15. Who wrote 'Frame and Fortune'?
16. How many players make up a team in rounders?
17. At which football ground is Gallowgate?
18. How is Edson Arantes Do Nascimento better known?
19. The compulsory figures are part of which cold sport?
20. What sport do the Washington Capitals play?
21. In which year of the 1980's did Joe Louis die?
22. Which cricket commentator is called 'Bumble'?
23. Which team finished third at France '98?
24. Which county cricket team is nicknamed 'Lightning'?
25. What nationality was Rene Lacoste?

JUMP

1. How many performers make up a trampoline team?
2. What sport is featured in the film 'White Men Can't Jump'?
3. How many water jumps are there in the 3000m steeplechase?
4. A netball team is comprised of how many players on court?
5. Kate Staples is a pole-vaulter but what is her Gladiator alias?
6. Which sport can be described as running off a hill or cliff looking for thermals to fill your canopy?
7. Andres Jacques Garnerin is credited with performing the first what in 1797?
8. Stefka Kostadinova is high jumper from which country?
9. In Ski jumping what is the Telemark position?
10. Which Cuban high jumper has dominated the event in the 1990's?
11. Ashia Hansen competes in which athletic event?
12. Jonathan Edwards was BBC Sports Personality of the Year in which year?
13. Who is 'His Airness'?
14. Is the long jump on the first or second day of the decathlon?
15. Staying with the decathlon, it includes the triple jump. True or false?
16. In basketball, when a player makes a jump shot whilst they're moving backwards what is it called?
17. Which singer was once rated the 85th best high jumper in the world with a personal best jump of 6ft 5½in?
18. Which man broke Bob Beamon's long jump record in 1991?
19. Which man won the 400m hurdles at the 1968 Olympics?
20. Yordanka Donkova was a famous hurdler from which country?
21. Edwin Moses won 122 consecutive contests in which event?
22. Which British woman won the Tokyo Olympics long jump title with a World record jump of 6.76m?
23. In 1973, Dwight Stones became the first man to set a World record in the high jump using which technique?
24. Who won the 110m hurdles at the 1998 European Athletic Championships making it his third successive victory?
25. What is the first event in the heptathlon?

QUOTES – WHO SAID...

1. "Do I not like that."
2. "I used to have a wild time with three girls until 5am. Now I am in training, it's five girls until 3am."
3. "We didn't have metaphor in our day. We didn't beat about the bush."
4. "When Michael Johnson's running, it's a fact that there are two races. At least I won the second race."
5. "When the seagulls follow the trawler, it is because they think that sardines will be thrown into the sea."
6. Which cricket legend, once dismissed for a low score, stood his ground and said: "The crowd has come to see me bat, not you bowl"?
7. "You can cut the tension with a cricket stump."
8. "Footballers' wives should be like small boys: seen and not heard."
9. "I was lucky to have the right horse on the right day."
10. "When you win the toss bat. If you are in doubt, think about it, and then bat. If you have very big doubts, consult a colleague and then bat."
11. "I didn't fully realise what I had let myself in for: the threat to my marriage, my sanity, my quality of life – that was all to come."
12. "When you shake hands with Don King, count your fingers afterwards to make sure they're all there."
13. Who said he didn't buy a railway ticket because: "If I buy a ticket, I spend twenty minutes signing autographs and I miss my train."
14. When his nation's football team beat England a commentator was moved to announce: "Lord Nelson, Lord Beaverbrook, Sir Winston Churchill, Sir Anthony Eden, Clement Attlee, Henry Cooper, Lady Diana. We have beaten them all ... Maggie Thatcher, your boys took a hell of a beating." Where was he from?
15. Who said this to Gareth Southgate: "I wish I could say I don't know how it feels, but I'm afraid I do."
16. "If he could pass a betting shop as well as he passes a football, he'd be one hell of a player." Which player was Brian Clough describing?
17. "If I win, I'm French. If I lose I'm American."
18. Who was fined for saying: "I wouldn't send my mother-in-law to Pakistan"?
19. When Joe Louis died who said this: "I idolised Joe. I just paid lip service to being the greatest – Joe was the greatest."
20. Which golfer said: "My family was so poor they couldn't afford any kids. The lady next door had me."
21. Which well-known Aussie said: "I don't want to do the batsman permanent injury, just to cause him concern, to hurt him a bit."
22. "Cricket was the easiest game in the world to take over. Nobody paid the players what they were worth."
23. "Footballers are only interested in drinking, clothes and the size of their willies."
24. Who said this about Linford Christie: "What can you say about him that hasn't been said before. He's slow and he's got a small penis"?
25. "So Arsenal have signed Arsene Wenger because his name sounds a bit like the club. How long before Man Utd sign Stefan Kuntz?"

MIXED BAG 34

1. How many West Ham players played in the 1966 World Cup final?
2. Judo and aikido are derived from which other martial art?
3. Who became World Heavyweight Champion in 1908 by beating Tommy Burns?
4. At which circuit does the Austrian Grand Prix take place?
5. Who lost in the 1999 Rugby World Cup final?
6. In baseball where do the Rangers come from?
7. Andy Irvine was a Scottish great in which sport?
8. Antonio Rattin was a footballer from which country?
9. Which number is between '8' and '14' on a dartboard?
10. In sailing what is left?
11. What is Ronaldo's shirt number for Brazil?
12. Who wrote the book 'Nice one Cyril'?
13. Which racing driver was BBC Sports Personality of the Year in 1986?
14. The Brewers come from which place in baseball?
15. Who is Paula Abdul's famous father?
16. Brooke Shields used to be married to which tennis star?
17. The Winter Olympics of 1984 were held in which city?
18. In the decathlon, what is the first event held on the second day?
19. WD is what position on a netball court?
20. Love Street is the venue for which football team?
21. Which golfer won the most Majors in the 20th Century?
22. Royal Ascot is held in which month?
23. Cycling was first governed by the ICA. What does it stand for?
24. Before France '98, how many times had Japan reached the World Cup Finals?
25. In which year did Don Bradman retire as Australia's cricket captain?

GENERAL KNOWLEDGE 2

1. Which NFL team has a 'D' on the side of their helmets?
2. Barry Briggs was a speedway star from which country?
3. What does BMI mean fitness-wise?
4. When was the New York marathon first run: 1960, 1970 or 1980?
5. Which famous US Golf course named its holes after flowers, trees and shrubs found near the holes?
6. Which World Heavyweight Boxing Champion was born on 10th January 1949 in Marshall, Texas?
7. Which football team is associated with Gigg Lane?
8. Which rugby league player has the nickname 'Chariots'?
9. When West Ham won the 1980 FA Cup, which London team did they beat in the final?
10. In 1989 which English Classic horse race was held in Scotland?
11. Gordon Greenidge and the late Malcolm Marshall both played for which county cricket team?
12. What did the KR stand for in Hull KR?
13. Vinnie Jones was a hod-carrier before joining Wimbledon. True or false?
14. The Preakness Stakes is a horse race held at which course?
15. The Centenary Test took place in 1976. True or false?
16. Bobby Moore and Pele play POW's in which film?
17. Which football club had a groovy 1970's hit with 'Funky City'?
18. Which golfer claimed he was twenty-one before he knew Manual Labour wasn't a Mexican?
19. Joel Garner gave his cap from the Old Trafford Test in 1984 to which umpire?
20. Is handball an Olympic sport?
21. The Scottish Grand National is held at which course?
22. Stuart Pearce, Chris Waddle and Gareth Southgate all appeared in which advert?
23. Tony Knowles was a sex symbol from which sport?
24. What is the first stroke in a medley swimming race?
25. Which county cricket team are known as 'Phoenix'?

FOOTBALL MANAGERS

1. Graham Taylor started his managerial career at which club?
2. After being sacked by Birmingham City, Barry Fry became manager and chairman of which club?
3. Harry Redknapp was manager of which club before West Ham?
4. Who was the first non-Irishman to manage Northern Ireland?
5. Which manager was the first this century to achieve the League and Cup double?
6. 'Big Mal' is a nickname for which extrovert 1970's manager?
7. Who resigned as manager of Birmingham City in 1998 for a couple of days after his family had been verbally abused?
8. Which famous Liverpool manager died in 1981?
9. Don Revie left the England job to manage which other country?
10. What nationality is Arsene Wenger?
11. When did Alex Ferguson become Man Utd manager: 1985, 1986 or 1987?
12. Tommy Docherty said this about whom: "He can't run, he can't tackle and he can't head a ball. The only time he goes forward is to toss the coin"?
13. Which well-known English manager had a near-fatal car accident in 1990?
14. Which manager of distinction co-wrote the Hazell detective stories?
15. "If Everton were playing down at the bottom of my garden I'd draw the curtains" was a quote from which fooball-mad manager?
16. Brian Clough won the European Cup with which club?
17. Which larger-than-life manager said this: "You're not a real manager unless you've been sacked"?
18. As at the beginning of the 1999 season, how many spells had Howard Kendall had as manager of Everton?
19. Who managed the 1998 World Cup winners?
20. Which manager do you associate with Scribes nightclub?
21. Who replaced Don Revie as manager of Leeds Utd but lasted only 44 days?
22. Who did Alf Ramsey succeed as England manager?
23. "Do I not like that" is a phrase connected with which manager?
24. Which Arsenal manager persuaded London Transport to change the local tube station name from Gillespie Road to Arsenal?
25. Who succeeded Bob Paisley as Liverpool manager in 1984?

IRISH SPORT

1. Which snooker player is known as the 'Hurricane'?
2. How many points is a goal worth in hurling?
3. What is the GAA?
4. Niall Quinn left which club to join Sunderland?
5. Jack Charlton became the manager of the Republic of Ireland in which year?
6. In rugby what position does Keith Wood play?
7. How many gold medals did Michelle Smith win at the Atlanta Olympics?
8. Who was known as the 'Clones Cyclone'?
9. Which woman won the London Marathon in 1998 at her first attempt?
10. Who was the captain of the 1974 Lions?
11. Man Utd bought Roy Keane from which club?
12. Don Fardon sang a song called 'Belfast Boy'. Who was it about?
13. The Irish Grand National is held at which Irish racecourse?
14. In which event did Mary Peters win a gold medal at the Munich Olympics?
15. In which year did Dennis Taylor beat Steve Davis on the final black to win the World Snooker Championship?
16. At the first World Athletics Championships which Irishman won the 5,000m?
17. How many World Cup Finals tournaments did George Best play in?
18. What was Ollie Campbell's rugby position?
19. How old was Norman Whiteside when he became a full Northern Ireland International?
20. Who is the only Irishman to win the Tour de France?
21. How many people make up a Gaelic Football team: 11, 13 or 15?
22. Which woman won the 5,000m and 10,000m at the 1998 European Athletics Championships?
23. In which city is Tolka Park?
24. Who did Barry McGuigan defeat in 1985 to become World Featherweight Champion?
25. Who was Michael Schumacher's team-mate during the 1998 and 1999 seasons?

MIXED BAG 35

1. 'Field of Dreams' is a film about which sport?
2. Which country lost in the 1958 World Cup final?
3. Which cricketer won the BBC Sports Personality of the Year award in 1975?
4. In the NBA where do the Grizzlies come from?
5. The Nick Owen Lounge can be found at which football club?
6. Lennox Lewis won an Olympic boxing gold medal for which country?
7. Who did Captain Mark Phillips marry in 1973?
8. 'Football Makes Me Laugh' is a book by which striker?
9. Actress Robin Givens married which famous sportsman?
10. Which French Classic horse race is always held on the first Sunday in October?
11. Silly mid-on and silly mid-off are positions in which game?
12. Is the field of play in softball bigger than that in baseball?
13. Which horse won the Cheltenham Gold Cup three times in succession in the 60's?
14. 190 lbs is the top weight in which boxing division?
15. What is the last event in the triathlon?
16. Tommi Makkinen is a star in which sport?
17. Which man won the 1500m in a World record time at the 1960 Olympics?
18. How often is the university boat race contested?
19. What nationality is Rubens Barrichello?
20. In which year was Ascot built?
21. Which lacrosse team has more players on the field of play: men's or women's?
22. When Little Polvier won the Grand National in 1989 how old was he: 12, 13 or 14 years old?
23. Who did Frank Bruno defeat to win the World Heavyweight title?
24. In tennis which gender competes for the Davis Cup?
25. Graeme Souness played international football for which country?

GOALIES 2

1. Which number does a goalie normally wear?
2. Which existentialist philosopher and writer was a keen goalkeeper in his youth?
3. Tony Coton left Man City to join which club?
4. In 1989 who became the first million-pound goalkeeper, moving from Bristol Rovers to Crystal Palace?
5. Pat Jennings was a goalkeeper for which country?
6. Which keeper performed the 'Scorpion Kick' at Wembley?
7. The tabloids started calling which turquoise shell-suit wearer 'the Son of God'?
8. Which former Liverpool goalie served in the Rhodesian army?
9. How old was Dino Zoff when he won he captained Italy to the World Cup?
10. Which goalkeeper was sent off against Coventry City in 1998 without even stepping on the pitch?
11. Jose Luis Chilavert is a goalie from which country?
12. Pope John Paul II played as a goalie in his youth. True or false?
13. Which Russian became the first goalie to win the European Footballer of the Year?
14. What was Peter Bonetti's nickname?
15. Charlie Chaplin was a name for a reserve keeper for which team between the wars?
16. Italy's first choice goalie for France '98 was ruled out 10 days before the contest started. Who was he?
17. Which son of a former Millwall goalie won an Winter Olympic gold medal for Britain?
18. Liverpool bought Ray Clemence in 1967 from which club?
19. Which Celtic player was the Republic of Ireland goalie at the 1994 World Cup?
20. Blackburn Rovers bought Tim Flowers from which club?
21. Who wrote the book 'Goalkeepers Are Different'?
22. Brad Friedel played for which country at France '98?
23. When did Peter Shilton make his league debut?
24. Which infamous German goalkeeper hacked down Patrick Battiston during a 1982 World Cup semi-final?
25. Which young Aston Villa goalkeeper replaced the veteran Jimmy Rimmer in the opening minutes of the 1982 European Cup final and played a blinder?

MOTOR RACING

1. Which son of a famous politician got lost in the Paris-Dakar Rally?
2. Which race hit the news in 1955 when 80 people died after Pierre Levegh's car catapulted into the crowd?
3. Which Canadian Indy Car driver tragically died during a race in 1999?
4. In which American state is Daytona?
5. What is NASCAR an acronym for?
6. In 1957 who became Formula One World Champion at the age of 46?
7. Thierry Sabine created which famous rally?
8. Which actor starred in the film 'Days of Thunder'?
9. In 1998 who won the Neste Rally of Finland for the fifth successive time?
10. Janet Guthrie became the first woman to qualify for which famous American race in 1977?
11. What is the BTCC?
12. When was the first Monte Carlo rally held?
13. Which racing driver won the 1992 BBC Sports Personality of the Year?
14. In which county is Donnington Park?
15. When was the first Le Mans 24-hour race held?
16. Who was the first non-American to win the Indy 500?
17. The Paris-Dakar rally doesn't start in Paris. Where does it start?
18. In America what is the NHRA?
19. Colin McRae joined which rally team in 1991?
20. Nigel Mansell joined which actor's Indy car team when in America?
21. Which of Stirling Moss's sisters achieved a second and a third place in the RAC Rally?
22. In 1998 the British Touring Car Championship took place at which track?
23. Jeff Bridges plays a hero in which 1973 film?
24. Tommi Makinen is a rally driver from which country?
25. "In my sport the quick are often listed among the dead." This is a quote from which motor racing World champion?

MIXED BAG 36

1. In American Football where do the Rams come from?
2. Teddy Sheringham left which club to join Man Utd?
3. Which team lost in two World Cup finals in the 80's?
4. The Kansas City Wizz is a team in which sport?
5. Which boxer later claimed he threw his World Heavyweight title fight in 1915 to Jess Willard?
6. In rugby union, what positions do numbers 6 and 7 play?
7. When did Barry McGuigan win BBC Sports Personality of the Year?
8. In American Football where do the Lions come from?
9. 'This Time' was England's World Cup song in which year?
10. Who won the US Masters in 1997?
11. In which sport would you shoot hoops?
12. Which darts player is known as 'Barney Rubble'?
13. What is the second event in the triathlon?
14. Which number is either side of '16' on a dartboard?
15. What is the last event in the decathlon?
16. In netball what position wears G?
17. The Winter Olympics took place at which venue in 1972?
18. Alexi Nemov is a name associated with which highly athletic sport?
19. 'Superbrat' was the nickname given to which tennis star?
20. Which Frenchman scored 28 points in his country's 43-31 defeat of New Zealand in the 1999 Rugby World Cup?
21. In which year did Glenn Hoddle become England manager?
22. In baseball where do the 'Twins' come from?
23. How long in minutes is a game of rugby union?
24. The Champion Hurdle is raced at which course?
25. In which year did Amsterdam host the Summer Olympics?

PREMIERSHIP

1. Who plays at Pride Park?
2. When Andy Cole left Newcastle Utd for Man Utd which player went the other way as part of the deal?
3. Which club chairman is known as 'Deadly Doug'?
4. Ian McMillan became the first official poet of which football club?
5. The Cliff is the training ground of which club?
6. When Blackburn won the Premiership, who were the 'SAS' who scored their goals?
7. Which player missed most of the 1997-98 season but was reinstated as captain of Man Utd in 1998?
8. 'Premiership Passions' was a TV show that followed the fortunes of which club?
9. In 1992 Andy Turner became the youngest player to score in the Premiership aged 17 years 166 days. Which club was he playing for?
10. In winning the 1997-98 Premiership how many league games did Arsenal lose all season?
11. Which teams were the first to appear on Sky TV's Monday Night Football?
12. Matthew Harding was a fan and part owner of which club?
13. In 1996 Fabrizio Ravanelli was signed by which club?
14. When Blackburn won the Premiership who was their manager?
15. Which Sheffield Wednesday player knocked over a referee during a Premiership match in 1998?
16. Directors Freddie Shepherd and Douglas Hall were reported as ridiculing the fans and players of which club?
17. Brian Little resigned from which club in February 1998?
18. Alan Curbishley managed which club into the Premiership in 1998?
19. The first man to score five goals in a Premiership match was Andy Cole, but against which team?
20. Who became the second man to score five goals in a single Premiership match in 1999?
21. Ruud Gullit's last Premiership game in charge of Newcastle was against which club?
22. Which Premiership team of 1998-99 sometimes came out to the song 'When the Red Red Robin comes bob-bob-bobbing along'?
23. Who was the first player to play for five different Premiership clubs?
24. Which team was the first to have nine goals scored past them in a Premiership match?
25. Who was the first player to score 100 goals in the Premiership?

GERMAN SPORT

1. Nicholas Keifer is a name linked with which sport?
2. Who was known as 'Der Bomber'?
3. Michael Schumacher drove for which team before Ferrari?
4. What is Michael Schumacher's brother's name?
5. Who became the first German to win the Tour de France?
6. Which golfer missed the putt which would have won the 1991 Ryder Cup?
7. The German Grand Prix takes place at which venue?
8. Who played 103 times for his country scoring, fourteen goals?
9. Which two German cities have hosted the Summer Olympics?
10. How many times have West Germany lost in the World Cup final?
11. Who was the coach of the 1974 World Cup winning side?
12. Which two Germans contested the 1991 Men's Wimbledon final?
13. Katerina Witt is a name associated with which sport?
14. Who is known as the 'Albatross'?
15. In 1930 which German won the World Heavyweight Boxing Championship after his opponent was disqualified?
16. Who was Germany's coach at France '98?
17. Who became the first German man to win the Wimbledon singles title?
18. Which German man won the Wimbledon singles title in 1991?
19. In 1988 which woman won the Wimbledon singles title for the first time?
20. Westfalon Stadion is the home ground of which football club?
21. Uwe Rosler played for which English football team?
22. Which sport, first played in Germany around 1890, is similar to football but instead of using your feet, hands are used?
23. Germany won the most medals at the 1998 European Athletics Championships. True or false?
24. Why did West Germany not go to the 1980 Olympics?
25. Otto Lilienthal is regarded as the modern pioneer of which airborne sport?

MIXED BAG 37

1. Lennox Lewis fought Frank Bruno for the World Championship in which year?
2. How long is a game of football in minutes?
3. In baseball where do the Red Sox come from?
4. Which country lost the 1990 World Cup Final?
5. In rugby union, 12 and 13 normally play in which positions?
6. In American Football where are the Chargers from?
7. What was England's 1990 World Cup song?
8. Who did France lose to in the 1998 rugby union Junior World Cup Final?
9. Who won the 1996 US Masters?
10. Which number is between '9' and '5' on a dartboard?
11. The pole vault is an event in the decathlon. True or false?
12. Where was the first Greyhound Derby held?
13. Which female athlete was the 1964 BBC Sports Personality of the Year?
14. In which year did Steffi Graf first win the Wimbledon singles title?
15. In Australian Rules Football how many points is a 'behind' worth?
16. How long is an Olympic size swimming pool?
17. What position do numbers 2 and 5 play in rugby league?
18. The Winter Olympics took place at which venue in 1964?
19. Who was the first woman to hold World, Olympic, Commonwealth and European titles at the same time?
20. 140lb is the top weight in which professional boxing division?
21. In which field events do you have a cage?
22. What athletic distance do you associate with Roger Black?
23. Man Utd bought David May from which club?
24. Ulla Lindkvist became the first female World Champion in which sport?
25. Who is the only other England player apart from David Beckham to be sent off at the World Cup?

TV 1

1. Which Trevor, a former West Ham player, is now a radio and TV commentator?
2. 'The Full Motty' was about whom?
3. Sir Paul Fox created which programme, shown on the BBC every year?
4. American Dick Button invented a famous TV show which pitted athletes from different sports against each other. What was the show called?
5. 'Fantasy Football' was shown on which channel during France '98?
6. Staying with 'Fantasy Football', which man always appears at the end of the show?
7. Which soap had a storyline involving four of its characters going to the France '98 final?
8. Kriss Akabusi replaced Roy Castle on which programme?
9. Which well-known snooker programme was axed by the BBC in 1986?
10. 'Hang Time' is an American TV show based around which sport?
11. Which sporting tournament was featured in the TV play 'My Summer with Des'?
12. When Judy Simpson was on 'Gladiators', what was her name?
13. Who was the original host of 'A Question of Sport'?
14. Which man had a TV show called 'Tee-Time'?
15. 'A Question of Sport' was first aired on TV in which year?
16. Who was the first man to win the BBC Sports Personality of the Year twice?
17. Whispering Ted Lowe used to commentate on which sport?
18. The BBC introduced Overseas Personality of the Year in which decade: the 1960's, 1970's or 1980's?
19. Kwai Chang-Caine was the main character in which TV show?
20. 'Match of the Day' has which former Liverpool and Scotland defender as a regular pundit?
21. Which TV show was the story of a Buddhist monk who had a price on his head and a master who was blind?
22. Frank Bruno fought in the first pay-per-view match in this country against which fighter?
23. The TV documentary 'An Impossible Job' focused on which manager?
24. James John Crossley is better known as which 'Gladiators' character?
25. The first match to be shown on 'Match of the Day' featured Liverpool against which London team?

GOLF 2

1. What nationality is Gary Player?
2. Kevin Costner plays a professional golfer in which film?
3. Who was the first golfer to win BBC Sports Personality of the Year?
4. What is the oldest golf tournament in the world?
5. Who won the British Open in 1997?
6. What is Tiger Woods' real first name?
7. 'Jack on my back' is a book by a former caddie of which man?
8. What number is the famous Road Hole at St Andrews?
9. What are the four golf Majors?
10. Which man won the British Open three times, the US Open four times and never turned professional?
11. In 1994 who won the British Open and the PGA?
12. What is the dancefloor?
13. What is the women's cup contested between the amateurs of the USA and Great Britain called?
14. 'Arnie's Army' were fans of which golfer?
15. In golf what is a bandit?
16. In golf what is the carpet?
17. Which British female golfer won the US Women's Open in 1997?
18. Until late 1999, Fanny Sunesson was which British golfer's caddy?
19. Percy Alliss was a well-known golfer but who is his son who also became a golfer and commentates for the BBC?
20. The 1998 season saw the rise of Se Ri Pak in the women's game but what is her nationality?
21. The World Matchplay takes place at which course?
22. In 1989 and 1990 which man won the US Masters?
23. The world's first golf club was formed in 1744. What was it called?
24. What is the R and A in golf?
25. The first British Open was held in which year?

MIXED BAG 38

1. In Olympic boxing what is the heaviest weight?
2. Who won the 800m at the Moscow Olympics?
3. 'This Sporting Life' is a film about which sport?
4. With which sport would you associate Greville Starkey?
5. Which was the first World Cup final to be decided on penalties?
6. Until 1990 which football team had won the old English First Division a record 18 times?
7. In athletics what is a PB?
8. Bandy is similar to which game but with more players?
9. What is a Caman in a game of shinty?
10. Which female athlete was BBC Sports Personality of the Year in 1972?
11. Which county cricket team occasionally plays at Cheltenham?
12. In 1998 the Gay Games took place in which country?
13. Lasse Viren was a famous runner from which country?
14. Ben Nevis was the Grand National winner in which year?
15. Tannadice is the home of which football club?
16. At which football ground would you find the North Bank?
17. In basketball where do the Celtics come from?
18. The 1994 Commonwealth Games took place in which country?
19. Uchi-Gake, Yorikiri and Utchari are all what?
20. Which golfer married Suzanne Danielle?
21. The film 'The Last Boy Scout' is based around which sport?
22. The Trotters is a nickname for which football team?
23. Which was the last club, before the start of the 1999-2000 season, to win the English League Championship or Premiership with an all-English team?
24. In Canoeing categories what does C stand for?
25. In which city is the Bislett Stadium?

HOCKEY

1. What nationality is Wayne Gretzky?
2. What is a 'Skin lid'?
3. In a game of ice hockey how many players make up each team on the ice?
4. With which American city would associate the Stars?
5. Which country won the Men's ice hockey Gold at the Nagano Winter Olympics?
6. A bully used to start a field hockey match. What starts a match now?
7. What colour card would a player initially be shown to warn him or her in field hockey?
8. Britain won the field hockey gold at the 1988 Olympics but who was the team's top scorer?
9. How many players make up a field hockey team?
10. A game of ice hockey is comprised of how many periods?
11. What is the NHL?
12. Which woman won the Wimbledon Singles Title and went on to captain her country at hockey?
13. What is known as 'the Pill'?
14. The first women's hockey World Cup was held in 1974 which European country won it?
15. How does a game start in Ice Hockey?
16. Which game is similar to hockey but played on an ice rink with 11 players a side?
17. How many players make up a roller hockey team?
18. Ice hockey was at one time an event at the Summer Olympics – True or false?
19. What is the IHF?
20. How is rink hockey better known?
21. What does FIH stand for?
22. How many zones are there on an ice hockey rink?
23. Britain's first ever gold medal at the Winter Olympics was in ice hockey – True or false?
24. What is Manchester's ice hockey team called?
25. What is Sheffield's ice hockey team called?

RUGBY LEAGUE

1. Jonathan Davies made his rugby league debut for which team?
2. In the 1968 Challenge Cup final, who missed an easy last-minute conversion which would have given Wakefield Trinity victory over Leeds?
3. What animal is associated with Leeds?
4. How many tackles are you allowed before you must hand over possesion in rugby league?
5. Wendell Sailor is a player from which country?
6. When was the Super League formed?
7. Which legendary rugby league commentator also presented 'It's a Knockout'?
8. How many players make up a rugby league team on the field of play?
9. In rugby league what position is the No 9?
10. In which decade was the game's name officially changed to Rugby League in this country?
11. Who won the first Super League?
12. True or false? The first Challenge Cup Final played at Wembley was in 1929?
13. Which nation won the first World Cup?
14. Who is known as 'Billy Whizz'?
15. If the Warriors were playing the Giants who would the two teams be?
16. The first Challenge Cup was played in which year?
17. Following on from the last question – which team won it?
18. Who plays at the Willows?
19. After eight successive Challenge Cup wins, who knocked Wigan out of the cup in 1996?
20. Who were the first rugby league side to enter the Middlesex Sevens?
21. Brian Bevan played seventeen seasons for which club?
22. The BBC televised their first rugby league game in which year?
23. Ellery Hanley was 17 when he signed for which club?
24. Who was the first England rugby league international to go on to play rugby union for England?
25. In 1998, who left St Helens to coach a new Super League team?

MIXED BAG 39

1. In American Football where do the Eagles come from?
2. Which boxer won the BBC Sports Personality of the Year award in 1967?
3. How many yards is the penalty spot from the goal-line in football?
4. Where were the 1968 Winter Olympics held?
5. Ben Crenshaw is a named linked with which sport?
6. Which football team has the nickname 'the Spirerites'?
7. In which sport would you find a Yokozuna?
8. At which ground do Luton Town play their home games?
9. Who is Thailand's national sporting hero?
10. Juan Manuel Fangio dominated Grand Prix racing in the early years, but what nationality was he?
11. 'Celtic Pride' is a film based around which sport?
12. The British Open in 1998 saw a play-off between which two golfers?
13. Which boxing great had the nickname, the "Brockton Blockbuster"?
14. Which horse won the Grand National in 1993?
15. In 1982 which Australian city hosted the Commonwealth Games?
16. Who won the Men's Wimbledon Singles Title in 1988?
17. Heaton Norris was a previous name of which football club?
18. How many golds did Roger black win in total at the European Athletics Championships: 4, 5 or 6?
19. The World Snooker Championship was won six times by which man in the 70's?
20. From 1982-87 which woman won the Wimbledon Singles Title?
21. In baseball where do the Giants come from?
22. The first World Cup at which there was a third place was held in which year?
23. At Royal Ascot the Gold Cup is always held on which day?
24. Which cricket county is known as the Dragons?
25. Where did the 1936 Winter Olympics take place?

ROYALTY

1. Princess Anne competed in which Olympics?
2. Which famous Australian bowler asked the Queen for her autograph at Melbourne in 1977?
3. Which race was extended by 385 yards so that the British Royal family could see the end of the race?
4. Which Olympic Gold Medallist was also a member of Haile Selassie's Imperial Guard?
5. In which year did Princess Anne win BBC Sports Personality of the Year?
6. The King George Chase is a horse race at which course?
7. Which sport do the Los Angeles Kings play?
8. Which Queen asked for Ascot to be built?
9. Who was the first Royal patron of Henley?
10. How did Frederick, Prince of Wales die in 1751?
11. Which King of Britain mistook a beater for a hare on a shoot and shot him in the kneecap?
12. With which Royal was Will Carling alleged to be close friends?
13. The Queen named two of her horses after which famous footballing brothers?
14. Who was the first reigning monarch to attend an FA Cup final?
15. What did Emily Davison do in 1913?
16. Alexander Obolensky was the son of a Russian prince and played which sport for England?
17. Which sport do you most closely associate with Prince Charles?
18. Which legendary Welsh fly-half of the late 60's and early 70's was universally known as the 'King'?
19. When Princess Anne appeared on 'A Question of Sport', who was her captain?
20. The King George VI and Queen Elizabeth Diamond Stakes are held at which racecourse?
21. Sarah Ferguson was alleged to be friendly with which Austrian tennis star?
22. When Man Utd fans talk about 'King Eric' who do they mean?
23. Kings Park is a ground in which South African city?
24. Prince Naseem Hamed first became World Champion at which boxing weight?
25. Which football team have the nickname the 'Royals'?

FAMILIES

1. Who is Venus Williams' tennis playing sister?
2. Rory and Tony Underwood both played which rugby position for England?
3. In America, Don and Donn Nelson are both names in which sport?
4. Canadians Gary and Paul Gait are identical twins who play the same sport. But which sport? Is it lacrosse, ice hockey or lumberjacking?
5. Name the Neville brothers' sister who plays netball for England?
6. Name the three Chappell brothers who all played cricket for Australia.
7. Which son of Johann Cruyff has played for Man Utd?
8. Mark Waugh is sometimes called 'Afghanistan'. Why?
9. Liam Botham had the choice of a career in two sports. What were they?
10. Young and Old Tom Morris dominated which sport in the 19th Century?
11. Which younger brother of Joe Davis won the World Snooker Championship eight times?
12. The fathers of Lancashire batsmen Graham Lloyd and Nathan Wood also played cricket for the county. What were their names?
13. The Maktoum family is associated with which sport?
14. John and Tracy who were the first brother and sister combination to win the mixed doubles at Wimbledon?
15. Rodney Marsh is a name linked with cricket but his brother Graham played which sport professionally?
16. Which two Spinks brothers both won Olympic boxing golds?
17. Who is Alec Stewart's dad?
18. Who said this about his mum after winning the World Snooker Championship: "Maybe she'll shut up about me getting a proper job now"?
19. Jackie and Bobby Charlton had a famous footballing uncle. What was his name?
20. In the 1989-90 football season Southampton had three brothers playing for them in the same team. Who were they?
21. Footballer John Moncur has two brothers who are both professionals in which sport?
22. Henry Cooper had a twin brother who also boxed. What was his name?
23. Sprinter John Regis has a cousin who played four times for England as a centre-forward. What is his name?
24. Which British 17-year-old swimmer went to the Moscow Olympics coached by her father Terry?
25. Neil Webb's wife is a journalist and commentator. What is her name?

MIXED BAG 40

1. What is the white ball called in bowls?
2. Richard Dunwoody was the jockey on the 1986 Grand National. What was the horse's name?
3. What is the heavier boxing weight: featherweight or super bantamweight?
4. Which football team used to play at the Goldstone Ground?
5. Who was the first New York team to win the Superbowl?
6. Who won the 1975 Cricket World Cup?
7. Small Heath Alliance was a previous name of which Midlands football club?
8. Which sport would you associate with Laxman Sivaramakrishnan?
9. Which Welshman won the World Snooker Championship in 1979?
10. Which two English football clubs share the nickname the 'Magpies'?
11. How old was Ali when he fought George Foreman: 30, 31 or 32?
12. Thomas Wentworth Wills invented which game in 1858?
13. Which female tennis player won the 1969 BBC Sports Personality of the Year award?
14. In which sport would you find a Killan Hold?
15. Which sport does Raymond Keane write about?
16. Whose nickname was 'The Manassa Mauler'?
17. Sri Lanka defeated England in 1998 in a test at which English ground?
18. Vijay Singh is regarded as the hardest working man in which sport?
19. Which famous baseball player had the forenames George Herman?
20. As well as Newcastle United, which other league team's ground is called St James' Park?
21. 'Shaggy' is the nickname for which former Liverpool midfielder?
22. Which is the oldest Football League club in England?
23. Where has the Tour de France finished every year since 1975?
24. Which Royal won Burghley in 1971 on Doublet?
25. Which South African born woman won a 400m silver for Great Britain at the 1968 Olympics but died in 1970?

EQUIPMENT

1. What is a box in cricket?
2. What do nasal strips help?
3. In gymnastics which piece of apparatus can be described as two horizontal bars arranged parallel to each other, with one bar 150 cm above the floor and the other 230cm above the floor with a 43 cm gap in between?
4. In boxing what is an Endswell?
5. Traditionally a cricket bat is made from which wood?
6. What are the legal dimensions of a cricket bat in inches?
7. What is a Mawashi in Sumo?
8. Which seven a-side game needs goals two metres high and three metres wide?
9. In which sport would you find Smallbore Standard, Smallbore Free and Bigbore?
10. How many white balls are there in a game of billiards?
11. The flatter the iron the further a golf ball will travel. True or false?
12. What is the Norwegian word for snow shoe?
13. In gymnastics which apparatus has two long bars set 42cm apart, supported 160cm above the floor?
14. Is a wicketkeeper's pad bigger or smaller than a batsman's?
15. What does a boxer wear to protect his mouth?
16. What is a stick in pool?
17. What would a cricketer use a 'coffin' for?
18. On which piece of equipment would a Gymnast do the flares?
19. A 'Cattie' is a term for which item used by an angler?
20. In hockey who wears kickers?
21. What do you call the person who carries golf clubs?
22. A golf ball is put on what when you play your first stroke at a hole?
23. In which sport would you use a spider rest?
24. What was first used at Wembley at a football international in 1955?
25. How many balls are there in a game of Carom billiards?

INVENTIONS
AND INNOVATIONS

1. Dick Fosbury revolutionised which event?
2. What did Gary Fisher and Tom Ritchey invent?
3. Which game did Tom Wills invent in the 19th century?
4. Dennis Amiss is regarded as the first person to wear what in cricket?
5. At which Olympics were sex tests first introduced for women?
6. The game of football was created and codified in which country?
7. Which game first came into being in a field in Cooperstown in 1839?
8. John Willes' sister is credited with changing cricket by doing what?
9. Which Australian came up with the idea of the 'Predator' football boot?
10. Which game was invented at the Duke of Beaufort's house in 1860 because it was raining outside and they wanted play without breaking any China?
11. Which heavyweight champion is credited with inventing the medicine ball?
12. When did football referees first use whistles?
13. Which game was created in Huddersfield at the George Hotel?
14. Ernst Killander invented which sport?
15. Which ball game did George Hancock invent in Chicago in 1887?
16. In which decade of the 20th Century was the first mechanical hare used at a greyhound meeting?
17. The Iroquios created it and called the game Baggataway. What is it more commonly called?
18. James Cribb invented which sport?
19. William Webb Ellis picked up a football and thus created which sport?
20. Korfball is a game that was originally invented in which country?
21. W G Morgan invented hockey in 1895. True or false?
22. Morihei Ueshiba founded which martial art?
23. Harry Hebner is credited with changing which swimming stroke to what we know today?
24. Taekwondo originates from which country?
25. What was Belgian Joseph Merlin the first to invent in 1760?

MIXED BAG 41

1. Cover drive, beamer and sweep are all terms from which sport?
2. How wide is the beam in women's gymnastics: 10cm, 15cm or 20cm?
3. How many Wimbledon singles titles did Martina Navratilova win?
4. Following on from the last question, who did she lose to in her last appearance in the final?
5. Masahiko Harada is a national hero in Japan. What is his sport?
6. How many times did Liverpool win the European Cup in the 1970's?
7. Is Tony McCoy a flat or national hunt jockey?
8. When was FIFA formed?
9. Which famous decathlete was on Mansfield Town's books in 1995-1996?
10. Hokutoumi is a name associated with which sport?
11. In husky racing how many dogs race in D class?
12. Which county did Jack Hobbs play for?
13. Brian Fletcher did it twice with him and Tommy Stack once. What was it?
14. Colin Hendry left Blackburn in 1998 to join which Scottish club?
15. Which quarterback gets kidnapped in the film 'Ace Ventura Pet Detective'?
16. How many times did Henry Cooper fight Ali?
17. In golf what is a banana ball?
18. At which Grand Prix track would you encounter the Ost and Sachs curve?
19. If a bookie talks about a 'splonk' what does he mean?
20. 112lb is the top weight in which boxing division?
21. The New Den is the home of which football club?
22. In cricket broadcasting, who is the 'Bearded Wonder'?
23. How many rounds did the 1975 Ali-Foreman fight last?
24. What is 11-12 inches long and can't weigh less than 50 grams
25. In which Spanish city did the 1998 European Indoor Athletics Championships take place?

NUMBERS

1. The Super 12 is a competition in which sport?
2. How many gold medals did Mark Spitz win at the Munich Olympics?
3. What was Maradona's shirt number?
4. How many yards are there in a furlong?
5. What number is triple Nelson?
6. Including the cue ball, how many balls are there in a game of snooker?
7. In American Football where do the 49ers come from?
8. What is the minimum number of matches that the winners of the Champions League will play during the 1999/2000 season?
9. Which number has '1' and '4' either side of it in a game of darts?
10. How many strikes do you need to bowl a perfect game in ten-pin bowling?
11. Which numbers are either side of '15' on a dartboard?
12. How many points is a goal worth in Australian Rules Football?
13. What is the perfect score in skating?
14. What is the maximum number of clubs permitted in a round of golf?
15. How old was Ali when he first became World Champion?
16. 10,122 is the total number of Test runs scored by which Indian batsman?
17. Rocky Marciano retired undefeated after how many fights?
18. What is the highest handicap rating in polo?
19. If you are 'Hanging 5' what are you doing?
20. What is the only number under 100 that can't be finished on with two darts?
21. If you score from 'downtown' how many points do you get?
22. In croquet singles how many balls do you get?
23. What is the maximum achievable break in snooker, if you were to start with a free ball?
24. In golf what are known as the red numbers?
25. Fives is a game that originates from Eton. True or false?

MIXED BAG 42

1. Who plays at White Hart Lane?
2. The 'Tug of War' is thought to originate from which country?
3. In which sport is The Cowdray Gold Cup contested?
4. In 1998 Simon Lessing became World Champion for the fourth time in which discipline?
5. At the 1984 Olympics Evander Holyfield won what colour medal for boxing?
6. Which Yorkshire Football team has the nickname the 'Bantams'?
7. The Derby is a horserace for colts only. True or false?
8. Sugar Ray Robinson fought which other famous boxer 5 times?
9. In which decade was the first US Golf Masters held: 1920's, 1930's or 1940's?
10. All aerobics courses have to be approved by the RSA. What is it?
11. The King's Stand Stakes is held at which meeting?
12. Bloomfield Road is the home of which seaside football team?
13. Gloucestershire played in the very first cricket County Championship. True. or false?
14. Sergei Shalibashvil died in 1983 from a sporting accident, but how?
15. At which Olympic Games were eleven Israeli athletes killed?
16. Roger Bannister rowed for Oxford in the boat race. True or false?
17. Was Rod Laver left or right handed?
18. In Hong Kong and China which form of exercise is practised by many people and involves performing slow-moving exercises smoothly?
19. John Newcombe was a tennis star from which country?
20. At what boxing weight did Floyd Patterson win an Olympic title?
21. In American Football where do the Redskins come from?
22. Which country does former Formula One World Champion Emerson Fittipaldi come from?
23. What is a face in gambling terms?
24. Which sport involves throwing 40lb stones on ice?
25. Which county did WG Grace play for?

WORLD CUP 2

1. Henry Kasperczak was the coach of which team at France '98?
2. Who knocked England out of the 1970 World Cup Finals?
3. Which South American country hosted the first World Cup?
4. In which year did the Germans first win the World Cup?
5. How many World Cup Winners' medals did Pele receive?
6. Which Argentine player scored a hat-trick on his World Cup Finals debut in 1994?
7. Which coach won the 1994 World Cup?
8. At which World Cup did East Germany beat West Germany?
9. Which was the first World Cup contested between the hosts and the holders?
10. Which was the first country to win three World Cups?
11. Which country were the first to lose in two World Cup finals?
12. How many times have Jamaica made it to the World Cup finals?
13. Who was the toothless member of England's 1966 World Cup winning squad?
14. Dorado was the first man to do what?·
15. In 1995 which country won the Women's World Cup?
16. Who was FIFA President from 1920 to 1954?
17. Which German scored fourteen goals in total at the 1970 and 1974 World Cup Finals?
18. Who was the first man to both manage and captain a World Cup winning team?
19. Before France '98 who were the last team to win on home soil?
20. Which player made his World Cup debut aged 17 years and 41 days?
21. Who finished fourth at the 1990 World Cup?
22. Brazil and Germany have never met in a World Cup Finals match. True or false?
23. Who was the last Englishman to appear in a World Cup final?
24. Who beat Argentina in the opening match of the 1990 tournament, beat Columbia in the second round and were finally knocked out by England in the quarter-finals?
25. Which player was joint top-scorer in the 1994 tournament despite the handicap of his team, Russia, being knocked out in the first round?

TIE-BREAKS 1 - NEAREST THE BULL

1. How high in centimetres is a hurdle in the women's 100m race?
2. Bobby Moore was England football captain for how many games?
3. The longest game at Wimbledon took place between Pancho Gonzales and Charlie Pasarelle in 1969. How many games in total did the match last?
4. What is the distance in feet between the bases in baseball?
5. Pele won 92 caps for Brazil scoring how many goals?
6. At what age did Monica Seles first attain the World No1 spot?
7. In which year was Arsenal Football Club formed?
8. How many red cards were given at France '98?
9. How many yellow cards were shown at France '98?
10. How many goals were scored at France '98?
11. Muhammad Ali fought how many professional bouts?
12. How many professional bouts did Sugar Ray Robinson fight?
13. The oldest English Football League club is Notts County. In which year was it formed?
14. When were the first Wimbledon championships held?
15. The Melbourne Cup was inaugurated in which year?
16. Dario Gradi became Crewe Alexandra manager in which year and month?
17. How many centimetres is a horsevault in women's gymnastics?
18. Exactly how old was Mike Tyson when he first became World Heavyweight Champion?
19. In men's gymnastics how high above the floor is the Horizontal Bar?
20. The Boston Marathon was first run in which year?
21. What was Gary Sobers' Test batting average?
22. How old was Jimmy Greaves in years and days when he scored his first goal for England?
23. San Francisco's Candlestick Park was built in which year?
24. Jesse Owens held the World long jump record for how long?
25. How long are the parallel bars in gymnastics?

MIXED BAG 43

1. Which famous Liverpool and Wales striker was born on 20th October 1961?
2. The Olympic flame was introduced at the 1928 Olympics. True or false?
3. Patrick Rafter is a tennis player from which country?
4. Major League is a film about which sport?
5. Ligaments join bone to what?
6. David Elleray is a schoolmaster and an official in which sport?
7. Darren Gough plays cricket for which county?
8. Which country won the most gold medals at the 1998 European Athletics Championships?
9. The top six teams compete for the Craven Shield in which sport?
10. 'My Road To Victory' chronicles the career of which Tour de France winner?
11. Which female athlete won the BBC Sports Personality of the Year in 1963?
12. What are the fewest points one has to win to win a set in tennis?
13. In a nine-ball pool set what colour is the No5?
14. Which weight is above Strawweight?
15. In which decade was UEFA formed?
16. What is the maximum number of members possible in a bobsleigh team?
17. Which Dutchman won the Wimbledon singles title in 1996?
18. Who did Paul Gascoigne make his England debut against?
19. Ali defeated who in 1980 to win the World Heavyweight title?
20. Before moving to a new stadium, which football team played at Leeds Road?
21. Jahangir Khan is a name connected with which sport?
22. Which football team was once called Ardwick?
23. What nationality is Gabriella Sabatini?
24. In American sport who is MJ?
25. What does RHR stand for in fitness terms?

GYMNASTICS

1. How many disciplines are there in men's gymnastics?
2. What nationality is Nadia Comaneci?
3. At the 1996 Olympics which female American gymnast vaulted with a twisted ankle to give the US the team gold?
4. Which Czech female gymnast concluded her career by winning four golds at the Mexico Olympics?
5. Which woman was the first to score a perfect ten in gymnastics?
6. What does 'overcooked' mean in gymnastics?
7. Which TV presenter and former international gymnast's dad once managed the Welsh football team?
8. Which 19th Century French gymnast gave his name to a garment?
9. Who was the female captain of the British gymnastic team at the Moscow Olympics?
10. How many disciplines are there in women's gymnastics?
11. Which smiling female gymnast won three golds and a silver at the 1972 Olympics?
12. Who became the first British man to win a medal at the World Gymnastic Championships in 1993?
13. Between 1956 and 1964 who won 18 Olympic medals, of which half were gold?
14. In what type of gymnastics do you perform with balls, hoops or clubs to music?
15. How long is the beam in gymnastics: 4, 5, or 6 metres long?
16. Suzanne Dando appeared in which James Bond film?
17. Gymnastics was an event at the very first Modern Olympics. True or false?
18. Are the Gymnastic World Championships held every 2 or 4 years?
19. What is the IGF?
20. Both men and women compete on the same size mat when competing in the floor competition. True or false?
21. What nationality is the gymnast Olga Korbut?
22. Which piece of apparatus is 110cm high, 163cm long with two raised handles in the centre?
23. Johann Friedrich is regarded as the first teacher of modern gymnastics techniques, dating from 1776, but which country was he from?
24. Following the break-up of the Soviet Union Vitali Scherbo competed for which country?
25. How high are the rings suspended from the floor: 200cm, 250cm or 300cm?

Answers to TIEBREAKS 1 – NEAREST THE BULL

1. 83.8cm *2.* 90 *3.* 112 *4.* 90ft *5.* 77 *6.* 17 *7.* 1886 *8.* 22 *9.* 254 *10.* 171 *11.* 61 *12.* 201 *13.* 1862 *14.* 1877 *15.* 1861 *16.* 1983 May *17.* 120cm *18.* 20 Years 4 months and 22 days *19.* 255cm *20.* 1897 *21.* 57.78 *22.* 19 years 86 days *23.* 1960 *24.* 25 years and 104 days *25.* 350cm long

ALL-ROUNDERS

1. Who was the first woman to score over 7,000 points in the Heptathlon?
2. Who played cricket for England, won an FA Cup winners' medal and held the World long jump record?
3. Which man had 24 England appearances for the England rugby union team, won the TV 'Superstars', was a good basketball player, a fine 400m hurdler and has taken up rowing in later life?
4. Which great Welsh rugby player won the 1966 Junior Wimbledon title?
5. How many events are there in the heptathlon?
6. Which England all-rounder's father was once captain of the Kenyan cricket team?
7. Which man, who was once on Arsenal's books, won the silver medal for the decathlon at the 1999 World Athletics Championships?
8. Who won the heptathlon title at the 1998 European Athletics Championships?
9. Name the five events that make up the modern pentathlon?
10. How many Olympic golds did Daley Thompson win?
11. Kapil Dev was a great all-round cricketer from which country?
12. The heptathlon first became an event at which Olympics?
13. Sir Garfield Sobers was an all-rounder for which Test side?
14. Which nationality is the decathlon champion Dan O'Brien?
15. In the 1912 Olympics, which future World War Two General was fifth in the modern pentathlon?
16. What is the first event of the first day of the decathlon?
17. In which year did Daley Thompson win BBC Sports Personality of the Year?
18. What is the first event in the triathlon?
19. In 1998 who became World Triathlon Champion for the fourth time?
20. Which Dallas Cowboys receiver won the 100m gold in the 1964 Olympics?
21. Michael Jordan retired from basketball for two years to play which other sport?
22. Denis Compton played cricket for England and football for which London club?
23. Judi Doull represented which country at cricket, hockey and basketball?
24. New Zealand Test cricketer Martin Donnelly, who died in 1999, played one rugby union international for which country?
25. Charlotte Dodd won Olympic silver for archery, played hockey for England and won which famous tennis tournament five times?

MIXED BAG 44

1. Who won the 1999 Charity Shield?
2. Who was the IAAF President who died in 1999?
3. In 1952 Philip Wills became the first Briton to be World Champion in which airborne sport?
4. John Snow played for which cricket county?
5. Vijay Singh is a golfer from which country?
6. 31 miles 123 yards is the distance of which Olympic event?
7. Which former footballer is Leslie Ash married to??
8. The Ipswich Witches play which sport?
9. Which Welsh rugby team play at Eugene Cross Park?
10. What nationality is Bjorn Borg?
11. 175lb is the top weight in which boxing division?
12. Who was the only woman to win gold for Britain at the 1998 European Athletics Championships?
13. The Minnesota Timberwolves play which sport?
14. Marc Rosset is a tennis player from which country?
15. The decathlon has two jumping events on the first day. What are they?
16. Which numbers are either side of '14' on a dartboard?
17. What does LTA stand for?
18. The Rose Bowl is a trophy in which sport?
19. Which football team plays at the Riverside Stadium?
20. What was Barry John's rugby position?
21. What is the ABA?
22. In America the Hambletonian is competed for in which sport?
23. In which sport would you compete for the Waterloo Cup?
24. Ballroom dancing will be included for the first time in the 2000 Olympic Games. True or false?
25. Which baseball team plays at Jacob's Field?

GROUNDS, COURSES AND VENUES

1. The Twin Towers are associated with which ground?
2. The Derby is held at which racecourse?
3. What is France's new national stadium called?
4. During the Five Nations in 1998 and 1999, Wales didn't play their home matches at Cardiff but at which venue instead?
5. In which city is Madison Square Garden?
6. Which country could play their home football matches at Ninian Park?
7. Yankee Stadium is called the house that who built?
8. England played football against which country in 1998 at the Wankdorf Stadium?
9. Which sport's World Championship is held at the Lakeside Country Club?
10. Wembley Stadium was built in which decade of the 20th Century?
11. Which Grand Prix takes place at Hockenheim?
12. Where is the Sha Tin Racecourse?
13. Where do Surrey play most of their home matches?
14. Which baseball team play at Shea Stadium?
15. In which country would you find Rasunda Stadium?
16. At which Australian stadium could you watch a match from 'The Hill'?
17. Which country was the first to host the World Cup twice?
18. Which venue was named after the first man to fly over the Mediterranean?
19. England play their home rugby union matches at which stadium?
20. Which gridiron team plays at Candlestick Park?
21. At which American stadium would you find the 'Green Monster'?
22. Which course hosted the 1999 British Open?
23. Which was the first capital city to host the Winter Olympics?
24. The Cricket World Cup has been hosted the most times by which country?
25. If the First World War had not taken place, where would the 1916 Olympics have been held?

SPORTING FILMS

1. Which sport is featured in the film 'Eddie'?
2. Which film is about the Jamaican bobsleigh team?
3. "Build it, they will come" is a line from which film?
4. What was the name of the horse in the film 'National Velvet'?
5. Which football stadium is the subject of a 1930's murder mystery film?
6. In which 1998 film do Samantha Janus, Gary Olsen and Neil Morrisey star?
7. 'Chariots of Fire' was about two British athletes competing at which Olympic Games?
8. 'When We Were Kings' is a film about which famous fight?
9. Derek Pringle was an extra in which Oscar winning film?
10. Which film is about a rugby team who crash in the Andes?
11. In 'Escape To Victory' which Polish international who played for Man City appear?
12. Which future World Heavyweight Champion featured in 'Rocky V'?
13. Which sport is featured in Spike Lee's film 'He Got Game'?
14. 'The Olympiad' was the official documentary of which Olympics?
15. Dee Hepburn proves to be the best player on the school football team in which film?
16. Until 1998 how many Rocky films have been released?
17. Sean Bean plays Jimmy Muir in which film?
18. Which man starred in the film 'Le Mans'?
19. 'Mighty Ducks' and 'Mighty Ducks II' are two quality films centred on which sport?
20. Gary Cooper portrayed which man in the film 'Pride of the Yankees'?
21. What was the sequel to 'The Hustler' called?
22. Tommy Lee Jones played which bigoted baseball legend in a self-titled film?
23. 'Below The Belt' is a film about women's wrestling. True or false?
24. Is 'The Championship Season' a film about basketball, ice hockey or baseball?
25. What number shirt does Michael Caine wear in 'Escape To Victory'?

MIXED BAG 45

1. Which martial art will make its debut at the 2000 Olympics?
2. In how many world title fights did Ali fight under the name Cassius Clay?
3. In 1983 which Canadian scored the first ever maximum break at the World Snooker Championships?
4. Between 1961 and 1990 a win in Formula One was worth how many points?
5. Former England cricket captain Tony Greig was born in which country?
6. 118lb is the top limit in which boxing weight?
7. Which famous English striker was born on 20th February 1940?
8. Was the 1996 Paralympics the 10th, 15th or 20th games?
9. Who became Middlesbrough manager in May 1994?
10. Which is the only golf Major to be hosted at the same venue every year?
11. What is the racing highlight of Royal Ascot?
12. Wilson Kipketer now runs for Denmark but where was he born?
13. In cricket what does MCC stand for?
14. Which NBA team plays at the Forum?
15. Fencing has been a sport at every Olympic Games. True or false?
16. ELO Ratings are used in which game?
17. How many men make up a male lacrosse team?
18. At which Olympics did Tony Nash and Robin Nixon win gold for Great Britain in the two-man bobsleigh?
19. 'Semi-Tough' is a film about which sport?
20. Who threw his Olympic gold medal in a river after being refused service in a restaurant because he was black?
21. What sport do the Penrith Panthers play?
22. Which football club are known as 'The Posh'?
23. What nationality was Ayrton Senna?
24. Which country hosted the Lacrosse World Championships in 1998?
25. In husky racing how many dogs race in C Class?

NATIONAL HUNT

1. Which man was Champion Trainer every season between 1986 and 1995?
2. Which horse won the Gold Cup for the third consecutive year in 1966?
3. Which horse won the Grand National in 1996?
4. How many fences are there in the Cheltenham Gold Cup: 22, 24 or 26?
5. In 1983, which Irish jockey did the unique double of the Champion Hurdle and the Gold Cup on Dawn Run?
6. Who was the first man to ride 1000 winners under national hunt rules?
7. Which famous trainer was born on 29th May 1945?
8. In 1983 which man trained the first five horses in the Cheltenham Gold Cup?
9. What is the minimum trip in a national hunt race: one mile, two miles or three miles?
10. Which horse won the Cheltenham Champion Hurdle in 1998 by a record twelve lengths?
11. Which horse was the first to win the Cheltenham Gold Cup and the Grand National in the same year?
12. Jump jockeys are generally heavier than their flat racing counterparts. True or false?
13. Dessie was a reference to which horse?
14. The King George VI Chase takes place at which course?
15. Who is Mark Pitman's famous mother?
16. In the 1981-82 season which two men were joint Champion Jockey in national hunt racing?
17. Which trainer is generally referred to as the 'Duke'?
18. Which jump jockey has the nickname 'Muttley'?
19. The Cheltenham Gold Cup was first held in which decade: 1920's, 1930's or 1940's?
20. Which man, in 1989, became the first to ride 200 winners in a season?
21. Jodami won the Cheltenham Gold Cup in which year?
22. Which former jockey, who is now a writer and TV pundit, was born in Swindon in 1952 and was Champion Jockey seven times?
23. The Whitbread Gold Cup is held at which course?
24. All horses carry the same weight in the Cheltenham Gold Cup. What weight?
25. The King George VI Chase is held on which day over Christmas?

Answers to SPORTING FILMS

1. Basketball 2. Cool Runnings 3. Field of Dreams 4. Pye 5. Highbury 6. Up n'Under 7. Paris 1924 8. The Ali/Foreman Rumble in the Jungle 9. Chariots of Fire 10. Alive 11. Kazymir Deyna 12. Tommy Morrison 13. Basketball 14. Berlin 1936 15. Gregory's Girl 16. Five 17. When Saturday Comes 18. Steve McQueen 19. Ice Hockey 20. Lou Gehrig 21. Color of Money 22. Cobb 23. True 24. Basketball 25. Number 3

COLOURS

1. What does a red flag indicate in the javelin?
2. Gary Player always wore which colour?
3. If you pot the black by mistake in a game of pool, what happens next?
4. What has gold in the centre then moving outwards red, blue, black and finally white?
5. What is the emblem on the All Black rugby shirt?
6. The Brown Bomber was the nickname of which boxer?
7. Which football club was once called the Black Arabs?
8. 'Blue Juice' is a film based around which sport?
9. What type of shirt does the King of the Mountains wear in the Tour de France?
10. How many red balls make up a game of snooker?
11. Man Utd said they couldn't see each other whilst losing at Southampton. What colour were their shirts?
12. Which American Football team plays at Lambeau field?
13. Red Grange is a name associated with which sport?
14. The Red Boys are a football club from which country?
15. The Cincinatti Reds and the Boston Red Sox both play which sport?
16. In a game of American pool what number is on the black ball?
17. Which cricket team is known as the Red Rose county?
18. How many points is the blue worth in a game of snooker?
19. In rugby's Super League who are the Blue Sox?
20. In which country was England all-rounder Craig White brought up?
21. What was Lucinda Green called before she married?
22. Alan Green mainly commentates on which sport?
23. If a horse is called green what does it mean?
24. Dave 'Boy' Green is a name associated with which sport?
25. The Little Brown Jug is a trophy from the USA in which sport?

MIXED BAG 46

1. Which club did Bill Shankly leave to take over as Liverpool manager?
2. Guy the Gorilla was a nickname for which cricketer?
3. Matt Biondi is a name associated with which sport?
4. How many times did Red Rum win the Irish Grand National?
5. The US Masters takes place at which venue?
6. What nationality is Jacques Villeneuve?
7. Which famous venue is in New York on 33rd West and 8th Avenue?
8. Who was born Rocco Francesco Marchegiano?
9. Which whirlwind-like snooker player was born on 2nd May 1962?
10. Newton Heath was the former name of which famous football club?
11. Which English cricket ground is called the 'Home of Cricket'?
12. Which country always comes first during the Opening Olympic ceremony?
13. Highbury is the home of which football club?
14. In 1974 rugby league devalued a drop goal from what to one point?
15. Which famous boxing Middleweight was known as 'Manos De Piedra'?
16. How many times did Ken Rosewall win the Wimbledon singles title?
17. Kevin Keegan left Liverpool for which club?
18. When Steffi Graf won the Wimbledon singles title in 1991, who did she beat in the final?
19. Which football club was once known as Singers FC?
20. Which man won both the 200m and 400m at the Atlanta Olympics with a running style compared to Forrest Gump?
21. The Iroquois Cup is competed for in which sport?
22. Who was the first footballer to be knighted in this country?
23. Which sport does the ICC control?
24. What did the Roman Emperor Theodosius abolish in 393AD?
25. Which Manchester club would you associate with Colin Bell?

LONG DISTANCE

1. In which film does Tom Hanks run and run and run and run?
2. How long is the marathon in kilometres?
3. In Ancient Greece which man ran the first marathon?
4. Which famous Liverpool manager said: "The Championship is a marathon not a sprint"?
5. Who was the first woman to hold world records at 5,000m, 10,000m and the marathon simultaneously?
6. Which English athlete, ahead of everyone after 26 miles of the 1954 Commonwealth Games marathon, still failed to finish the course?
7. Who won the 5,000m, 10,000m and the marathon at the 1952 Olympics?
8. Which athletics event was won in a time one hour faster in the 1980 Olympics than in the 1932 games?
9. Which marathon starts on the Verrazano Bridge?
10. Abdi Bile was born in which country?
11. Who was BBC Sports Personality of the Year in 1974?
12. Emil Zatopek ran for which country?
13. Which Australian was the first to break 28 minutes for the 10,000m?
14. In 1993 Wang Junxia knocked 42 seconds off which World record?
15. Which woman won the World Cross-Country title in 1998?
16. In 1953 which man was the first to run the marathon in less than 2 hours 20 minutes?
17. In the 1976 Olympics the British track and field team won only one medal, a bronze in the 10,000m. Who was the man?
18. Which Portuguese woman entered her first marathon in 1982 at the European Championships and won?
19. When was the first London Marathon held?
20. Why is the marathon 26 miles 385 yards long?
21. Which Paula finished second in the World Cross-Country Championship in 1998?
22. Who beat Lasse Viren's 10,000m World record by over 7 seconds in 1973?
23. Roberta Gibb was the first woman to run which marathon in 1966?
24. When was the first women's 10,000m run at the Olympics?
25. 'Running Brave' is a film telling the story of which American winner of the 10,000m at the Tokyo Olympics?

WATER SPORTS

1. In surfing what is 'Hanging 10'?
2. What does a surfer call a 'Shark Biscuit'?
3. Mike Hazelwood was a World Champion at which sport?
4. In Olympic diving there are three heights. What are they?
5. Elvis played a surfer in which 1961 film?
6. How can you tell the difference between the two teams in a game of water polo?
7. How many make up a team in water polo?
8. Slalom jumping and trick riding are three sections in which sport?
9. In surfing what is a 'Wipe Out'?
10. In which sport would you perform an 'Eskimo Roll'?
11. Richard Fox is a World Champion in which sport?
12. Martin Potter became the first Briton in 1989 to be a World Champion in which watersport?
13. The Harmsworth Trophy is associated with which sport?
14. A Kayak has a paddle with a blade at each end. True or false?
15. K4 is an Olympic category. True or false?
16. What is the WWSU?
17. Chris Snode represented Britain at the Olympics in which sport?
18. Who was the first British man to win the World Water Skiing Championships?
19. 'Big Wednesday' is a film about surfing. True or false?
20. 'Pauline A La Plage' is a film about which watersport?
21. Which snooker player was Australian Surfing Champion in 1950?
22. If you are 'shagging a doughnut' you are surfing. True or false?
23. Which British swimmer played a wind-surfer in a silent film called 'The Optimist'?
24. Hungary played Russia at water polo at the 1956 Games. Why was it a grudge match?
25. In sailing what is a 'Rubber Duck'?

MIXED BAG 47

1. How many bails are there on top of a set of cricket stumps?
2. In the NBA where do the Magic come from?
3. What odds are sometimes called 'Net' by a bookie?
4. Ryan Giggs' dad was a professional in which sport?
5. Which England bowler had an Autobiography called 'Cricket Rebel'?
6. The hosts of the Olympics always come in last at the Opening Ceremony. True or false?
7. What is the IAAF?
8. FC Porto is a football club from which country?
9. Which German city hosted the 1986 European Athletic Championships?
10. 'The Mighty Atom' and 'The Ghost with a Hammer in his Hand' were both nicknames for which boxer?
11. How many Olympic gold medals did Carl Lewis win?
12. Which baseball player is called 'Big Mac'?
13. Philippides died in 490BC. What did he create?
14. Derek Redmond married which swimmer?
15. When Great Britain won bronze in the four-man bobsleigh at Nagano, who was the driver?
16. How many people make up a shinty team?
17. John Arlott used to commentate on which sport?
18. In which American city would you find Wrigley Field?
19. Who won the first Everton / Liverpool derby?
20. How many points is a successful penalty kick worth in rugby union?
21. In which season were three points for a win introduced to English football?
22. Where is the Happy Valley racecourse?
23. Which football team used to play at Roker Park?
24. What odds are known by bookies as Enin?
25. In which year did Helsinki host the very first World Athletics Championships?

RULES AND REGULATIONS

1. The Cartwright Rules formulated in 1845 are used in which sport?
2. In which sport are you penalised for travelling?
3. Whose use of an aluminium bat caused MCC to change the laws of cricket?
4. What nationality is Jean-Marc Bosman?
5. "Brushes may be exchanged between players on the same team during a game, but a team broom may not be exchanged" is a law from which Olympic sport?
6. In which sport would you find the 'in-field fly' rule?
7. In 1912 keepers were restricted to handling the ball in their penalty area. What could they do before the new law?
8. In which year of the 1960's were substitutes allowed in football if a player was injured?
9. In tennis, if your serve touches the top of the net and goes over the other side what happens?
10. Which report recommended new rules on ground safety after the Hillsborough disaster?
11. In which sport must the ball be "spherical with a diameter of 38mm and shall weigh 2.5g"?
12. Name the famous English university credited with drawing up the first set of rules for football in 1848?
13. When was overarm bowling legalised?
14. Before 1910 what did you have to do to score a six in cricket?
15. What can't a base runner do after a batter has hit the ball in the air in baseball?
16. What was first issued in 1975 in England?
17. Is it possible to be run out off a no-ball in cricket?
18. Is it possible to be stumped off a wide in cricket?
19. What happens if a ball is hit into fair territory by a batter and then bounces off the field of play in baseball?
20. What is a 'walk' in baseball?
21. In cricket, how many runs are scored if the ball strikes a helmet placed behind the wicket-keeper for 'safe keeping'?
22. If a player strikes a post from a penalty and hits the resulting rebound into the back of the net is this a goal?
23. Can a player score directly from a corner?
24. Before penalties and the away goals rule were introduced in European cup-ties, matches went to extra-time and were then replayed. But what happened if the teams were still level?
25. How many ways can you be dismissed in cricket?

179

TIE-BREAKS 2 - NEAREST THE BULL

1. In which year were Blackburn Rovers formed?
2. When Alan Wells won the 100m Olympic title, what time did he run in the final?
3. Test cricket was first played in South Africa in which year?
4. In which year was netball invented?
5. In which year were Sheffield Utd formed?
6. Mr Frisk won the National in 1990 in what time?
7. In which year did Arsenal move to Highbury?
8. When did the first Everton / Liverpool derby take place?
9. In which year were Ipswich Town formed?
10. What was the official attendance for the 1950 World Cup final between Brazil and Uruguay?
11. On what date did Rocky Marciano announce his retirement?
12. Soldier Field is the home of the Chicago Bears. In which year was it built?
13. In which year were Barnsley formed?
14. How many golds did America win at the 1984 Olympics?
15. How many Grand Prix starts did Ayrton Senna make?
16. In which year were Aston Villa formed?
17. When was the first Challenge Cup final held?
18. How many Grand Prix starts did Niki Lauda make?
19. Jackie Stewart raced in how many Formula One races?
20. How long is the horse vault in gymnastics?
21. How many competitors took part in the first Olympics in 1896?
22. In which year were Sheffield Wednesday formed?
23. The King George V Gold Cup in show-jumping was first contested in which year?
24. When was the first cricket Test between England and Australia played on English soil?
25. In which year were Bolton Wanderers formed?

MIXED BAG 48

1. Who are the Cavs in the NBA?
2. National hunt trainers consider which race as the most important in the national hunt calendar?
3. In which country is the Sun City Golf tournament held?
4. In chess, how many pieces does each player start with?
5. Where were the fourth modern Summer Olympics held?
6. Who in 1970 got to keep the Jules Rimet trophy?
7. The Cotton Bowl is a trophy in which hard-hitting sport?
8. Lennox Lewis won Olympic boxing gold at which weight?
9. Arnold Palmer is a legend in which sport?
10. Which football team has the nickname the 'Bees'?
11. Jim Laker played cricket for Surrey but in which county was he born?
12. Who did Manchester City last beat in a European competition?
13. Tendons join muscle to what?
14. In American Football, where do the Bengals come from?
15. What positions do numbers 3 and 4 play in rugby league?
16. In boxing which weight is below heavyweight?
17. Which famous duo wrote an autobiography called 'Face the Music'?
18. In cricket who are known as the men in white coats?
19. In which American city would you find Busch Stadium?
20. Why was the 1979 Superbowl called 'The Yellow Ribbon Bowl'?
21. Ian Botham and Viv Richards both played for which cricket county?
22. Which rugby club do you associate with the ground Kingsholm?
23. Dennis Christopher and Dennis Quaid both starred in which cycling film?
24. Which Aussie starred in Liverpool's 1986 double winning team?
25. Which world famous boxer was born 17th May 1956

UPSETS AND UNDERDOGS

1. Who knocked Germany out of France '98?
2. What was the score in the France '98 final?
3. Mike Tyson was beaten by James Buster Douglas in which city?
4. Who owned 'Devon Loch'?
5. At which World Cup did America beat England 1-0?
6. In 1935 at which race did 2-1 favourite Golden Miller unseat his jockey at the first hurdle?
7. Which English boxer defeated Sugar Ray Robinson to become World Middleweight Champion?
8. In which year did Ingemar Johansson beat Floyd Patterson to win his Heavyweight title?
9. Who won the 1980 FA Cup Final?
10. Which team lost the 1973 FA Cup Final?
11. Who lost the US Masters in 1996 despite starting the final round with a six shot lead?
12. Which manager took Manchester United down in 1974?
13. In 1953 England were beaten 6-3 at home by which team?
14. Who won the America's Cup in 1985?
15. When Liverpool lost the 1988 FA Cup Final who beat them?
16. Which man was the odds on favourite to win the Wimbledon title in 1975?
17. Which man defeated Ali in 1978 for the world title?
18. At which ground did England pull off a remarkable victory in the Third Ashes Test in 1981?
19. Which 150-1 outsider won the 1986 World Snooker Championship?
20. Which country won the 1996 Cricket World Cup?
21. In the Challenge Cup final in 1998 who lost in the final?
22. Henry Cooper lost his last professional fight in controversial circumstances to which fighter?
23. Which country won the 1983 Cricket World Cup?
24. Who knocked Martina Hingis out of Wimbledon in 1999?
25. In 1982 which suave snooker player knocked out Steve Davis in the first round of the World Snooker Championship 10-1?

TV 2

1. Who were the first two captains of 'A Question of Sport'?
2. Who is the presenter of Channel Four's cricket coverage?
3. Which 18-stone snooker player split his trousers in a televised match in 1980?
4. Brain Jacks won 'Superstars' but what was his sport?
5. Before Sue Barker, who hosted 'A Question of Sport'?
6. Frank Skinner and David Baddiel took the mickey out of which footballer for having a 'pineapple' on his head?
7. Which actress played 'The Manageress'?
8. When Anneka Rice left 'Treasure Hunt' who replaced her?
9. 'Match of the Day' first came to TV in which year?
10. 'World of Sport' was shown on which TV channel?
11. Who replaced John Fashanu as the male presenter of 'Gladiators'?
12. Alf Garnett supported which football team?
13. Which former England bowler hosted 'Indoor League'?
14. Which brilliant show on ice did Dani Behr host?
15. Who was the bodybuilder who played the Incredible Hulk in the TV series?
16. In the run up to France '98 Gary Lineker had a show about the World Cup top scorers what was it called?
17. Which 1998 BBC1 series was about a female football team?
18. During the 70's if you were watching Kendo Nagasaki, what sport would you be watching?
19. Which teams contested the first live Football League match on TV?
20. Penelope Pitstop was always looking for help in which show?
21. Who hosts 'Friday Night's All Wright'?
22. Who is Angus Loughran better known as?
23. Danny Blanchflower refused to go on which programme?
24. In which year did the BBC introduce the Team of the Year award at the 'Sports Review of the Year'?
25. 'Screaming Reels' is a show about which sport?

MIXED BAG 49

1. Ballyregan Bob had 32 consecutive wins in which sport?
2. The Cherry Bowl is a trophy in American Football. True or false?
3. Which famous Australian swimmer was sent home from the 1964 Olympics after she went looking for souvenirs in the Emperor's apartments?
4. Which football team is known as the 'Hatters'?
5. In which sport can you be no-balled for throwing?
6. Which football team's supporters used to stand on the 'shelf' before all seater stadiums became law?
7. Ronnie O'Sullivan is a name connected with which sport?
8. Who was the first man to win back-to-back US Masters titles?
9. how many players make up a team in roller football?
10. The Oaks is run at which course?
11. What is the World governing body of football called?
12. Robbie Earle plays his international football for which country?
13. Gazza left which club to join Middlesbrough?
14. Which marvellous boxer was born on 23rd May 1952?
15. Which skater won the BBC Sports Personality of the Year in 1980?
16. Which former American Football player had a major role in the film 'Naked Gun'?
17. Which sport do the Sacramento Kings play?
18. Which London club is known as 'The O's'?
19. In baseball does the home team bat first or second?
20. Karen Briggs is a name associated with which martial art?
21. Which two football clubs contest the 'Old Firm' game?
22. In which sport might you win the Sugar Bowl?
23. In which year did India become a cricketing Test side: 1922, 1927 or 1932?
24. The Queen Elizabeth II Cup is a show-jumping contest for women only. True or false?
25. Northampton Town has a nickname associated with shoes. What is it?

CUPS AND TROPHIES

1. Which two teams compete every year for the Calcutta Cup?
2. What did Pickles the dog re-discover?
3. Golden Miller won which well-known horserace five times in succession?
4. What is the female equivalent of the Ryder Cup?
5. In which sport is the Lonsdale Belt awarded?
6. At which golf Major does the winner receive a Green Jacket?
7. In which sport is the Uber Cup contested?
8. Why is the Ryder Cup so called?
9. How is the 'Fall Classic' better known?
10. The Middleton Cup is a trophy contested in which exciting sport?
11. Which two countries are co-hosting the 2002 World Cup?
12. Which two teams competed in the Silk Cut Challenge Cup final in 1998?
13. For what feat is the Trophée Jules Verne awarded?
14. What trophy does the man of the match in the Challenge Cup final receive?
15. Which men's tennis trophy is competed for by countries rather than individuals?
16. What is the Cy Young Award for in baseball?
17. In 1998 who won the women's Rugby World Cup?
18. Which tennis event takes place at Flinders Park?
19. What is the World Bowl the European equivalent of?
20. When Denmark won the European Football Championships in 1992 they were a late entry because which country had been expelled?
21. In 1998 which English team won the European Super Cup?
22. What is the most coveted cup at the Henley Regatta?
23. The Stanley Cup is awarded to a winning team in which sport?
24. Roy Evans won only one trophy as Liverpool manager. What was it?
25. The Webb Ellis Cup is another name for which trophy?

TIE-BREAKS 3 -
BIRTHDAYS -
NEAREST THE BULL

1. Mike Tyson
2. Tiger Woods
3. Evander Holyfield
4. Muhammad Ali
5. Fatima Whitbread
6. Frank Bruno
7. Alex Higgins
8. David Gower
9. Olga Korbut
10. Linford Christie
11. Alan Shearer
12. Enzo Ferrari
13. Viv Richards
14. Steffi Graf
15. Roger Bannister
16. Pele
17. Jenny Pitman
18. Ellery Hanley
19. Paul Gascoigne
20. Michael Jordan
21. Jack Nicklaus
22. Martina Navratilova
23. Geoffrey Boycott
24. George Best
25. Tessa Sanderson

MIXED BAG 50

1. Sir Gordon Richards rode only one Derby winner. True or false?
2. What nationality is Georgi Kinkladze?
3. Which former 'Z Cars' actor wrote the screenplay for 'Chariots of Fire'?
4. 'The Chair' is a famous fence in which horserace?
5. 'Fly Me To the Moon' is a fanzine written by the fans of which football club?
6. In 1961 the World Skating Championship was cancelled after which team died in a plane crash?
7. How many players form a rugby union front row?
8. Which London football club are known as 'The R's'?
9. 160lb is the top weight in which boxing division?
10. In 1996 which man won the 100m Olympic title?
11. Which British city hosted the 1986 Commonwealth Games?
12. At which football ground can you watch the match from the Gwladys Street End?
13. Keke Rosberg was a Formula One World Champion from which country?
14. What position is the number 7 in a game of rugby league?
15. Which basketball legend played for the LA Lakers and was acclaimed as the master of the hook shot?
16. Which American Football team plays at the Mile High stadium?
17. Which former World Heavyweight Boxing Champion died in a plane crash in August 1969?
18. Who was 1996 BBC Sports Personality of the Year?
19. Which 'Wizard of Dribble' was born on February 1st 1915?
20. Which football team are known as the 'Quakers'?
21. Women competed at the first Commonwealth Games but in only one sport. What was it?
22. Tyrell Biggs was the first man to win Olympic gold at which boxing weight?
23. Kevin Keegan had a bad cycle crash when competing on which TV show?
24. Who won the 1999 baseball World Series?
25. The first non-American to win the USPGA Championship was Gary Player. True or false?

FOOD AND DRINK

1. Which team's fans sing: "Meat pie, sausage roll, come on ... give us a goal"?
2. What is a poached egg in golf?
3. Which famous England cricketer, during an MCC tour of India, was handed some caviar of which he said: "The blackcurrant jam tastes of fish"?
4. "When I was a wee boy I ate too many sweets and made matters worse by not cleaning my teeth. I lost my last teeth aged 28". Which dentally challenged sportsman said this?
5. In Japan, which sportsmen traditionally eat Chanko Nabe?
6. Which England football manager was compared to a turnip?
7. When Tony Adams admitted he was an alcoholic which of his team-mates said: "It took a lot of bottle for Tony to own up."
8. After scoring 174 runs in the Centenary Test at Melbourne in 1977, which man was sent 174 pork chops?
9. The Budweiser Bowl in the 1980's was a trophy contested in which sport?
10. 'Sour Grapes' is a fanzine written by the fans of which football club?
11. Who was the BBC Sports Personality of the Year in 1976?
12. Ivano Bonetti allegedly had his cheekbone fractured by a plate of what?
13. Which British athlete said this after the Atlanta games: "It was horrific and the food in the village was terrible. Now I am back home I can speak without getting lynched by the Americans"?
14. California surfer Tom Harvey is famous for creating what?
15. When the Old Christians rugby team crashed in the Andes how did they stay alive?
16. When Gazza was at Newcastle, which chocolate bar did fans throw at him?
17. In the Walkers Crisps advert who is the little girl talking about when she says: "Oh Gary"?
18. Which Danish international footballer was convicted of drink driving in 1988?
19. "It's Bavarian State law that beer isn't alcohol. It's a means of nutrition." This was a quote from which well-known German striker?
20. Which football team are nicknamed 'The Cherries'?
21. Susan Cheeseborough competed for Great Britain in which sport?
22. Which footballer had chapters in his autobiography called 'The First Drop', 'I Am An Alcoholic' and 'Drinking For England'?
23. Darryl Strawberry is a star from which sport?
24. In wrestling what does 'potato' mean?
25. Former Olympic figure skating champion Oksana Baiul crashed her car due to alcohol but what was her original excuse?

Answers to TIEBREAKS – BIRTHDAYS -NEAREST THE BULL

1. 30th June 1966 *2*. 30th December 1975 *3*. 19th October 1962 *4*. 17th January 1942 *5*. 3rd March 1961 *6*. 16th November 1961 *7*. 18th March 1949 *8*. 1st April 1957 *9*. 16th May 1955 *10*. 10th April 1960 *11*. 13th August 1970 *12*. 18th Febuary 1898 *13*. 7th March 1952 *14*. 14th June 1969 *15*. 23rd March 1929 *16*. 23rd October 1940 *17*. 11th June 1946 *18*. 27th March 1961 *19*. 27th May 1967 *20*. 17th February 1963 *21*. 21st January 1940 *22*. 18th October 1956 *23*. 21st October 1940 *24*. 22nd May 1946 *25*. 14th March 1957

SCOTTISH SPORT

1. The Braemar version is 19ft tall and weighs around 132lbs. What is it?
2. Graham Obree is a name connected with which sport?
3. Billy Bremner played the majority of his career for which English club?
4. Roberto Duran described which boxer as the best he ever fought?
5. Who is Monty?
6. Les Wallace was a World Champion in which sport?
7. Who was the World Grand Prix Champion in 1963?
8. Which snooker player earned the nickname the 'Wonder Bairn'?
9. Where do Scotland play their home rugby union matches?
10. Tell me the next line of this song: "O Flower of Scotland when we will see.."?
11. Ken Buchanan was World Champion at which weight?
12. Gavin Hastings' brother also played rugby for Scotland. What is his name?
13. Who scored a penalty for Scotland against Brazil in France '98?
14. Which motor racing champion was born on the 4th March 1936?
15. Who was Scotland's first World Darts Champion?
16. Who won BBC Sports Personality of the Year in 1973?
17. Which man played rugby for Scotland and won the 400m at the 1924 Olympics?
18. Which team plays at Fir Park?
19. Which 1980 Olympic gold medallist was called the 'Flying Scot'?
20. Richard Corsie was a World Champion in which sport?
21. John Collins signed for which English football club in 1998?
22. Which Scottish flanker was often described as the 'Big Kelso Farmer'?
23. Who was Alan Hansen's older brother, who played football for Scotland twice in 1972?
24. In 1996 which Scot became the first British man to beat Linford Christie over 100m in 10 years?
25. Which male athlete won the 200m at the 1998 European Athletics Championships?

MIXED BAG 51

1. The Coronation Cup race is run at which course?
2. Is the mat area for gymnastics in the floor discipline: 12m, 13m or 15m square?
3. In a game of pool what colour is the number 8?
4. Which football team plays at St Andrews?
5. 168lb is the top limit for which boxing weight?
6. Where was the penultimate Grand Prix of the 1999 F1 season held?
7. Which club was the subject of Hunter Davies' book 'The Glory Game'?
8. Which English Classic is raced at Epsom over 1 mile 4 furlongs?
9. Foil, epée and sabre are three categories in which sport?
10. How is the very fast ball game Jai Alai better known?
11. The Sam Maguire Trophy is awarded in which Irish sport?
12. In tennis what is the least amount of games you must win to secure a set?
13. When was the penalty kick invented in football?
14. Which football derby would have the Robins playing the Pirates?
15. Women compete for the Federation Cup in which sport?
16. Humphrey Bogart starred in a film called 'The Harder They Fall'. What was the sport?
17. What have Sunderland and Benfica got in common?
18. Who was the first professional to captain the England cricket team?
19. Which football team plays at Moss Rose?
20. In professional boxing what weight is above Super Featherweight?
21. When England won the 1966 World Cup who wore the No 6?
22. Norton is a famous bike name from which country?
23. The man who invented orienteering came from which country?
24. How many people make up a hurling team?
25. 'Cups For Cock-Ups' is a book about which football club?

SPORT MUSIC

1. The Matchroom Mob and Chas 'n' Dave performed which song?
2. "Where have you gone Joe Di Maggio" is a line from which Simon and Garfunkel song?
3. Chris Isaak could have been a professional in which sport?
4. Which big man sang 'We shall not be moved'?
5. 'Swing Low Sweet Chariot' is a song associated with which sport?
6. Which duo made Ravel's Bolero famous again?
7. The instrumental part of Fleetwood Mac's 'Chain' is associated with which sport?
8. Which of the Charlton brothers released a version of 'You'll never walk alone'?
9. Who toured the UK and Europe with his group The Knockouts in 1972?
10. 'He Got Game' is a song by which Rap act?
11. Which Radio One DJ has children named after Liverpool players?
12. The official song of France '98 was called 'The Cup of Life' who sang it?
13. 'I Believe I can Fly' is the theme tune to which film?
14. 'Don't come home too soon' is a song by which Scottish group?
15. Which baseball and gridiron star had a rap album called 'Prime Time'?
16. Nigel Kennedy supports which football team?
17. Which member of 60's pop group The Monkees had once been a jockey?
18. Staying with the 60's, in which New York stadium did The Beatles perform live?
19. Which football club would you associate with Elton John?
20. The Harlem Globetrotters are linked with which well-known song?
21. Which group had a No1 British single with the 'Eye of the Tiger'?
22. Which boxer's father was 3rd in 1970 Eurovision Song contest?
23. The Dark Destroyer is now a DJ. Who is he?
24. Shaquille O'Neal has released albums and has his own record label. What is his sport?
25. In 1990 the Scottish rugby team released which song?

SQUASH

1. What nationality is Jansher Khan?
2. Who was the first British man to be ranked No1 in the world?
3. Sarah Fitzgerald is a World Champion from which country?
4. What is the ISRF?
5. Can a player score on his opponent's serve?
6. How long in feet is an International singles court?
7. American Earl Riskey formulated which game similar to squash, but with wider, shorter rackets?
8. Which New Zealand woman won the British Open seven times in succession between 1984 and 1990?
9. Which Briton won six British Open titles?
10. In 1971, Sheffield had the first court in this country with which facility?
11. When were the first World Championships held?
12. Who won the first male championships?
13. Who won the first female championships?
14. In tournament play, how many points does it take to win a game?
15. Which coloured dot is normally used in tournaments: red or yellow?
16. Which public school is credited with the development of squash as boys queuing to play rackets would use any available wall while they were waiting?
17. If there were an accidental collision of players in a game what would the referee call?
18. Which ball has the highest bounce: blue or yellow dot?
19. What is the SRA?
20. If you cut the ball what does it do?
21. What does the term 'crowding' mean?
22. Of yellow, white and red spotted balls, which has the lowest bounce?
23. What is the ISPA?
24. Which squash player stormed off the TV show 'Superstars'?
25. Jonah Barrington was born in Ireland. True or false?

MIXED BAG 52

1. Where were the first Summer Olympics south of the equator held?
2. At one time this ball game was called 'Mush-Ball'. What do we know it as today?
3. Where was the first Asian Summer Olympics held?
4. Which football team plays at Edgeley Park?
5. All the Irish horseracing Classics are held at which course?
6. Jose Capablanca was a famous chess player from which country?
7. Curtis Strange is a name from which sport?
8. The Dallas Cowboys were originally called the Dallas Texans. True or false?
9. Tim and Tom Gullikson were twins from which sport?
10. Which music star played a boxer in the film 'Kid Galahad'?
11. In cricket what does 'lbw' stand for?
12. The America's Cup is in which sport?
13. How many of the following three counties played in the first County Cricket Championship: Kent, Surrey, Derbyshire?
14. Which team did Damon Hill drive for in 1998?
15. To complete a 147 break in snooker how many pots must you make?
16. How many people make up a team in Tug of War?
17. The 4th Summer Olympics took place at London. True or false?
18. Netball is derived from which other game?
19. How many bets are there in 'a Yankee'?
20. Carl Lewis was the first man to win two consecutive Olympic 100m finals. True or false?
21. Who won the Centenary Test: England or Australia?
22. How many times did Sugar Ray Robinson win the World Middleweight title: three, four or five times?
23. 126lb is the top weight in the Featherweight division. True or false?
24. The French Tennis Open is played on which surface?
25. Which football team plays at Easter Road?

TABLE TENNIS

1. Which British woman was five times runner-up in the World Table Tennis Championships?
2. A game is won by the first player to reach which score?
3. The Swaythling Cup is the world championship for which gender?
4. What are 'Pen Hold' and 'Shake Hands'?
5. In feet, how long is a table?
6. Tom Hanks plays a table tennis star in which film?
7. Which man won 25 English titles?
8. The International Table Tennis Federation was formed in which year?
9. Table tennis made its Olympic debut at which Olympics?
10. In 1929 which name associated with lawn tennis won the World title?
11. In 1936 two players met in the World Championship and took over two hours over the first point. True or false?
12. Richard Bergmann was a World Champion who became British. What was his original nationality?
13. What happens if your serve touches the top of the net when going over the net?
14. What is the ITTF?
15. What is a loaded ball?
16. Is backspin used mostly on attacking or defensive shots?
17. If you hit the ball deep what does it mean?
18. How wide is a table tennis table?
19. Will a high toss serve give more or less spin?
20. How tall is the net in inches?
21. The Seemiller grip is named after a champion from which country?
22. Ping-pong is a former name for table tennis. True or false?
23. In the history of the game who is James Cribb?
24. Which famous tennis player's dad won a table tennis tournament and as a prize chose a tennis racket at his son's request?
25. In 1997 which English city hosted the World Table Tennis Championships?

MIXED BAG 53

1. Preacher Curls exercise your legs. True or false?
2. What is the BEF?
3. Who was Princess Anne's first husband?
4. Which game consists of a team of twelve of which six are men, six women, and you have three zones in which you aim to score in a basket?
5. Archery was first seen as an Olympic event in which year?
6. Which number is between '19' and '16' on the dartboard?
7. After the red what is the lowest value ball in snooker?
8. In which sport do you score in the 'house'?
9. Which game involves a course of twelve hoops and a peg?
10. How tall is a netball hoop?
11. What is CV work when you go to a gym?
12. Which Scotland and Manchester United midfielder did Alex Ferguson describe as 'untrustworthy'?
13. Who is Tiger Woods' influential father?
14. Which boxer was known as the 'Hitman' and the 'Motor City Cobra'?
15. Which Barry is the man behind the Matchroom Organisation?
16. What sport do the Vancouver Grizzlies play?
17. How many people make up a team in volleyball?
18. Racquetball originates from America. True or false?
19. In softball what is the ISF?
20. Some countries stayed away from 1956 Olympics because the USSR had invaded which country?
21. The Breeders Cup is a contest for horses held in which country?
22. What is the highest possible dan in judo: 10th, 12th or 15th?
23. In which century was the Jockey Club formed?
24. Where is the National Hunt Gold Cup held?
25. Who did Manchester City fans call 'Kinky'?

Answers to MIXED BAG 52
1. Melbourne 1956 *2.* Softball *3.* 1964 Tokyo *4.* Stockport County *5.* Curragh *6.* Cuba *7.* Golf
8. False *9.* Tennis *10.* Elvis *11.* Leg before wicket *12.* Sailing *13.* All of them *14.* Jordan *15.* 36
16. 8 *17.* True *18.* Basketball *19.* 11 *20.* True *21.* Australia *22.* Five times *23.* True *24.* Clay
25. Hibernian

TRUE OR FALSE?

1. Michael Bolton nearly became a professional boxer instead of a singer.
2. Mary Decker Slaney was the matron of honour at Zola Budd's wedding.
3. Andre Agassi's dad was an Olympic rower.
4. Nude Beach Volleyball will make its Olympic debut at the 2004 Olympics.
5. Peter Beardsley could have been a professional model instead of a footballer.
6. Cassius Clay, as he was known, won an Olympic gold at Light Heavyweight.
7. The Winter Olympics in 1998 was the 18th games.
8. Surfers are more likely to be attacked by sharks if they have urinated in their wet suits.
9. Ear-pulling is an event in the Eskimo Olympics
10. Hurdles are exactly the same height in the men's 110m and 400m hurdles.
11. Ray Illingworth is a godfather to Devon Malcolm's children.
12. In the pole vault your maximum run up is 50 metres.
13. Walkers must maintain unbroken contact with the ground when in competition.
14. In billiards the red ball is never touched with the cue.
15. Rounders is a game derived from baseball.
16. JPR Williams was a junior tennis champion at Wimbledon.
17. Tonya Harding and Nancy Kerrigan released a single called 'Friends'.
18. Sugar Ray Leonard was never knocked out in his professional career.
19. Babe Ruth was originally a pitcher.
20. You can't be sent off in Australian Rules Football.
21. P T Barnum once owned Madison Square Garden.
22. O J Simpson's nickname as an American Footballer was 'Running Death'.
23. Monica Seles first won the Wimbledon singles title in 1996.
24. Roger Bannister's shirt number when he broke the four-minute mile was 40.
25. Jackie Stewart won three Formula One World titles.

MIXED BAG 54

1. What does YMCA stand for?
2. In 1998 which Grand National winner died 16 years after his greatest triumph?
3. Andre Joubert is a famous rugby player from which country?
4. Who was the first man to beat Mike Tyson in a professional fight?
5. Which NFL team has G on the side of its helmet?
6. 'Million Dollar Mermaid' is a film about which sport?
7. Nick Knight plays his cricket for which county?
8. The Varsity rugby match is played in which month?
9. Vladmir Smirnov died in 1982 by getting what in his eye?
10. Which football team plays at Prenton Park?
11. How many times was Ayrton Senna Formula One World Champion: 3, 4 or 5?
12. What nationality was the tennis player Arthur Ashe?
13. In darts which number is known as 'Double Top'?
14. In 1952 which country joined the ranks of Test cricketing sides?
15. What is the most attended sporting event every year, is free to watch and takes a month to complete?
16. In Ireland the Curragh is in County Kildare. True or false?
17. Which Brazilian became the first to score in every match of the World Cup tournament, scoring seven goals in six games?
18. Who wrote 'Fever Pitch'?
19. Can a batsman be bowled off a no-ball?
20. All Black Jeff Wilson has also represented New Zealand at which sport?
21. Who partnered Steve Redgrave to the gold medal at the 1988 Olympics?
22. Ian Botham left Somerset for which other county?
23. Eddie Macken was a top showjumper from which country?
24. Which famous swimmer announced in 1973 that he would retire and dedicate his life to Israel?
25. Which famous British Heavyweight released a single called 'Knock Me Down With A Feather'?

SPELLING

1. ZINEDINE ZIDANE (FOOTBALLER)
2. NOUREDDINE MORCELI (RUNNER)
3. EMIL N'TAMACK (RUGBY PLAYER)
4. ANDREI KANCHELSKIS (FOOTBALLER)
5. ADEDAYO ADEBAYO (RUGBY PLAYER)
6. STEFKA KOSTADINOVA (HIGHJUMPER)
7. MARK CALCAVECCHIA (GOLFER)
8. JAVED MIANDAD (CRICKETER)
9. SEVERIANO BALLESTEROS (GOLFER)
10. LASSE VIREN (RUNNER)
11. ARANTXA SANCHEZ-VICARIO (TENNIS PLAYER)
12. RUBENS BARRICHELLO (RACING DRIVER)
13. REINALDO NEHEMIAH (HURDLER / AMERICAN FOOTBALLER)
14. YEVGENY KAFELNIKOV (TENNIS PLAYER)
15. JAIRZINHO (FOOTBALLER)
16. JARMILA KRATOCHVILOVA (RUNNER)
17. INGRID KRISTIANSEN (RUNNER)
18. FANNIE BLANKERS-KOEN (DUTCH SUPER ATHLETE)
19. MICHAEL SCHUMACHER (GRAND PRIX DRIVER)
20. HAILE GEBRESILASIE (RUNNER)
21. MIKKA HAKKINEN (GRAND PRIX DRIVER)
22. VA'AIGA TUIGAMALA (RUGBY PLAYER)
23. MARTINA NAVRATILOVA (TENNIS PLAYER)
24. JOOST VAN DER WESTHUIZEN (RUGBY PLAYER)
25. YORDANKA DONKOVA (FEMALE HURDLER)

Answers to TRUE OR FALSE?
1. False *2.* False *3.* False (Boxer) *4.* False *5.* False *6.* True *7.* True *8.* True *9.* True *10.* False *11.* Very
False *12.* False (No limit) *13.* True *14.* True *15.* False *16.* True *17.* False *18.* True *19.* True *20.* True
21. True *22.* False *23.* False *24.* False (41) *25.* True

ONE - DAY CRICKET

1. In which year was the first Gillette Knockout Cup?
2. Who were the original sponsors of the Sunday League?
3. How many overs per side were Benson & Hedges Cup matches until 1996?
4. Which county won the first ever One-Day International?
5. What replaced the Benson & Hedges Cup in 1999?
6. Who was the first player to hit a double century in the Sunday League?
7. Which player holds the record for most sixes in a Sunday League innings?
8. Who was the first batsman to hit a century in a Gillette Cup final?
9. Which bowler did the hat trick twice in the 1989-90 Sharjah tournament?
10. Who, in 1998, became the first player to appear in 300 One-Day Internationals?
11. Which county won the first two Sunday League titles?
12. Which team scored 322 for 5 in a NatWest final and lost?
13. Which batsman hit 189 not out against England at Old Trafford in 1984?
14. As at the end of the 1999 season, which player holds the record for the greatest number of Benson & Hedges Gold Awards with 22?
15. Which player has been Man of the Match in NatWest finals for two different counties?
16. Which player hit the winning runs in all three England v Australia One-Day Internationals in 1997?
17. Which county has done the NatWest/B&H double twice?
18. In 1969 Somerset's Brian Langford recorded the Sunday League's most economical bowling figures, which have never been beaten. How many runs did he concede in his eight over spell?
19. Where was the first One-Day International played?
20. Which player hit 24 runs in one over for Lancashire in a 1971 Gillette Cup match at 8.45 pm?
21. The winners of the last B&H Cup final in 1998 also won the first one in 1972. Which county?
22. Up to the end of 1999, which bowler was the leading One-Day International wicket-taker?
23. Which insurance company sponsored the Sunday League between 1993 and 1998?
24. Which player hit 143 runs off just 66 balls in a CGU National League match at Chelmsford in 1999?
25. In 1998 which batsman passed Desmond Haynes' record of 17 One-Day International centuries?

MANCHESTER FOOTBALL

1. What was Manchester United's original name?
2. Where did they originally play?
3. When did they become Manchester United?
4. When did Ardwick FC become Manchester City?
5. Where did City play until 1923?
6. When did United move to Old Trafford?
7. What was the result of the first Manchester derby?
8. When did United first win the FA Cup?
9. Where was the final held?
10. Which City player shared the 1969 Football Writers' Footballer of the Year award?
11. Which United player won the same award in 1948?
12. Who did Bobby Charlton make his full debut against?
13. How many years separated United's seventh and eighth League Titles?
14. Which England cricketer once played on the wing for City?
15. Who was the first international to play for both United and City?
16. Who scored City's winner in the 1969 FA Cup final?
17. Who is the only player to have played for two different clubs in the same FA Cup competition?
18. Who scored a hat trick in the 1993 Old Trafford derby?
19. Which two future City stars both made their full debuts against the Blues?
20. Where did City win the 1970 European Cup Winners' Cup?
21. Where did City clinch the 1968 League title?
22. Who scored City's last-gasp equaliser in the 1999 Second Division Play-Off final?
23. Who scored the then quickest ever FA Cup final goal against City in 1955?
24. What have Peter Barnes, Sammy McIlroy and Wyn Davies got in common?
25. Who scored against his former club on his League debut in 1990?

ONE - DAY CRICKET
1. 1963 2. John Player 3. 55 overs 4. Australia 5. The B&H Super Cup 6. Alistair Brown (203) 7. Ian Botham (13) 8. Geoffrey Boycott 9. Wasim Akram 10. Mohammed Azharuddin 11. Lancashire (1969 & 1970) 12. Sussex 1993 (lost to Warwickshire) 13. Viv Richards 14. Graham Gooch 15. Dermot Reeve 16. Adam Hollioake 17. Lancashire (1990 & 1996) 18. none (8-8-0-0) 19. Melbourne 1970-71 20. David Hughes 21. Leicestershire 22. Wasim Akram 23. AXA 24. Andrew Flintoff 25. Sachin Tendulkar

Alphabetical Index

Answers to MANCHESTER FOOTBALL

1. Newton Heath *2.* North Road, Monsall *3.* 1902 *4.* 1894 *5.* Hyde Road *6.* 1910 *7.* City 2, Newton Heath 5 (1894) *8.* 1909 *9.* Crystal Palace *10.* Tony Book *11.* Johnny Carey *12.* Charlton Athletic (1956) *13.* 26 years *14.* Patsy Hendren *15.* Billy Meredith *16.* Neil Young *17.* Stan Crowther 1958 (he was given special dispensation following the Munich Air disaster) *18.* Andrei Kanchelskis *19.* Colin Bell for Bury and Francis Lee for Bolton Wanderers *20.* Vienna *21.* St. James' Park, Newcastle *22.* Paul Dickov *23.* Jackie Milburn for Newcastle *24.* They all played for both United and City *25.* Ryan Giggs v. City (he signed for them as a teenager)

ALSO AVAILABLE FROM EMPIRE PUBLICATIONS

I'm Not God ... I'm Just The Referee
by Roy Entwistle

Paperback - RRP £7.99

ISBN: 1 901746 01 0

Roy Entwistle, for 30 years a referee in Manchester's amateur leagues, has been there, done that and booked the defender. Now he reveals the secret art of refereeing; the pressures affecting refs at all levels of the game, and the antics of players, supporters and managers, all of whom believe that they know best.

Cups for Cock-ups - The Extraordinary story of Manchester City F.C.
by Ashley Shaw - photographs by Michael Clarke

Paperback - RRP £8.99

ISBN: 1 901746 04 6

"IF CUPS WERE AWARDED FOR COCK-UPS THEN YOU WOULD NOT BE ABLE TO MOVE IN CITY'S BOARDROOM"

So said Francis Lee during his first spell at the club. How ironic it is that the man who uttered those very true words, was, in the eyes of many, to be responsible for multiplying the club's problems during a nightmare four-year stint as chairman.

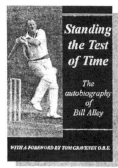

Standing the Test of Time -
The autobiography of Bill Alley

Hardback - RRP £16.95
ISBN: 1 901746 06 2

Originally suppressed by the Test and County Cricket Board in 1985, this is the controversial autobiography of respected Test umpire and former Somerset cricket legend Bill Alley, revised and updated to include recent developments in the world game.

"*Splendid autobiography*" - Robin Marlar, *The Cricketer*

"*Strong opinions and no lack of humour*" - David Foot

S.F. Barnes - His Life and Times
by Andrew Searle

Hardback - RRP £14.95
ISBN: 1 901746 00 3

The extraordinary story of the legendary cricketer Sydney Francis Barnes.

"*A SUPERBLY CONSTRUCTED BIOGRAPHY*" ROBIN MARLAR, THE CRICKETER

"*A GOOD ANGRY READ*" ALISTAIR McLELLAN, INSIDE EDGE

"*COMPULSIVE READING FOR ANYONE INTERESTED IN THE HISTORY OF THE GAME OF CRICKET*" ROSS REYBURN, THE BIRMINGHAM POST

The Encyclopaedia of Scottish Cricket
Written and Compiled by David W. Potter

Paperback - RRP £9.99
ISBN: 1 901746 07 0

A collection of fascinating anecdotes, facts and figures covering all aspects of cricket in Scotland from the earliest days to the present.

"*Delightful*" - Daily Mail.

"*Scottish story of splendid obscurity*" - The Independent.

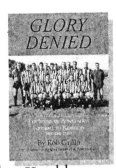